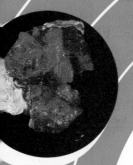

SPECIAL PROJECTS
BOOK PLUS INDEX
AND BIBLIOGRAPHY

FUNK & WAGNALLS new
ENCYCLOPEDIA
OF SCIENCE

FUNK & WAGNALLS, INC.

HOW TO USE FUNK & WAGNALLS NEW ENCYCLOPEDIA OF SCIENCE

Volumes 1 through 21 have information printed on the front covers, spine, and title pages that make it easy to find the articles you want to read.
- Volume numbers are printed in all three places in Volumes 1 through 21.
- Letter breaks — $\frac{COL}{DIA}$ — are printed in all three places in Volumes 1 through 21. The letters above the line are the first three letters of the first article title in the volume. The letters below the line are the first three letters of the last article title in the volume.
- Page breaks — $\frac{351}{438}$ — are printed on the spines and title pages of Volumes 1 through 21. They provide the page numbers of the first and last text pages in the volume.

Articles are arranged alphabetically by title in Volumes 1 through 21. Most titles are printed in **BOLD-FACE CAPITAL** letters. Some titles are printed in even larger letters.
- Some titles are not article titles, but refer you to the actual article title. Within articles you will find *See* or *See also* other article names for further information. All of these references to other articles are called cross-references.
- Most article titles are followed by a phonetic pronunciation. Use the Pronunciation Guide on page vi of Volume 1 to learn the correct pronunciation of the article title.
- At the end of most articles are two sets of initials. The first set identifies the person who wrote the article. The second set identifies the special consultant who checked the article for accuracy. All of these people are listed by their initials and full names and position on pages v and vi of Volume 1.
- ◣ This symbol at the end of an article indicates that there is a project based on the subject of the article in the Projects, Bibliography & Index volume. The project is found under its article title, and all of the project article titles are arranged alphabetically on pages 1 through 64 of the Projects, Bibliography & Index volume.

The Projects, Bibliography & Index Volume contains three sections. Each is an essential part of the encyclopedia.
- Projects based on articles in the encyclopedia are found in the first section. Each is both entertaining and educational. Each is designed for use by a student and for parental participation if desired.
- Bibliography reading lists in the second section list books under general scientific categories that are also titles of major articles. Each book listed is marked with either a YA (Young Adult) or J (Juvenile) reading level indicator. YA generally applies to readers at the junior high level or higher. J applies to readers at grade levels below junior high school.
- Index entries for all article titles plus many subjects that are not article titles are found in the third section. Instructions on using the Index are found at the start of the Index section in the Projects, Bibliography & Index volume.

PROJECTS FOR VOLUME 1

ABACUS

Materials Needed:
picture frame,
string,
thumbtacks,
beads or buttons

Procedure:
1. Cut 5 pieces of string the same length (long enough to cross the picture frame with an extra 7.5 cm [3 in] on each end for making knots).
2. Place 5 evenly spaced thumbtacks along each side of the frame.
3. Slide 7 beads (or buttons) onto each string.
4. Tie the end of one string to the first thumbtack at either side of the frame. Continue tying the strings until you have all 5 strings tied across the frame.
5. On all strings, move 5 beads to the left side of the frame and 2 beads to the right side.
6. Take an additional piece of string twice as long as one of the first 5. Placing your frame so that the 5 strings are left to right, tie this new piece around the frame at the top, about half way across.
7. With the dividing string tied to the top of the frame, bring it down to the next string and tie a knot. Continue down to the next string and tie another knot. Work down to the bottom of the frame until knots have been tied with all the strings. Then tie the string around the bottom of the frame. You now have the dividing line of the abacus.

Your abacus should now have 5 strings extending from left to right with 5 beads to the left side of the dividing string, and 2 beads to the right.

Holding the abacus before you, the bottom string represents units. The five beads on the left have a value of 1 each. The two beads on the right have a value of 5 each.

The second string represents values of tens. Each bead on the left represents 10 units. Each on the right represents 50 units.

The next string is hundreds, the next thousands, and the fifth string represents ten-thousands (A).

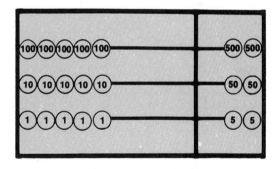

A.

You are now ready to try a problem. Count 4 on your abacus. To do this, push 4 beads from the left side of the bottom string to the center (B).

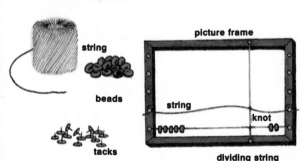

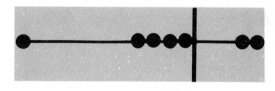

B.

Now, add 5. Do this by pushing one bead from the right side to the center (C). You have just completed an addition problem. $4 + 5 = 9$.

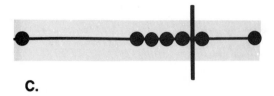

C.

Next, subtract 6. Do this by moving the 5 unit bead on the bottom right back to the frame edge, and move one unit bead on the left back to the frame edge (D). You have now solved a subtraction problem. $9 - 6 = 3$.

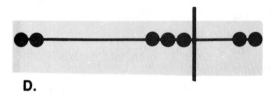

D.

Next, add 8. Move the 5 unit bead on the right to the center, and move three 1 unit beads from the left to the center. You will find only two to move. Move them. Your abacus will appear as in (E).

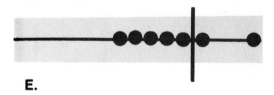

E.

You have a value of 10. Move the five 1 unit beads on the left to the frame and move the one 5 unit bead on the right back to the frame. Replace their value of 10 by moving one 10 unit bead on the second string from the left to the center. You still have a value of 10. Now move the one 1 unit bead to the center (F). You have a total of 11. ($3 + 8 = 11$)

F.

Now add 295. Just as in regular addition, add 5 first by moving a 5 unit bead from the right to the center (G).

G.

Next, add 90 by moving a 50 unit bead from the second string right, and four 10 unit beads from the left (H).

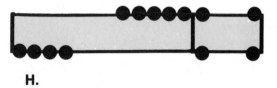

H.

Last, add the 200 by moving two 100 unit beads on the third string. You now have a total of 306 (I).

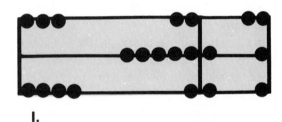

I.

Since the value on the second string is equal to 100, you can adjust your abacus by moving the beads to the frame edges, and replace the value by moving one 100 unit bead from the third string (J).

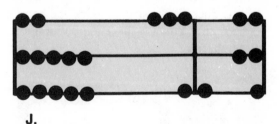

J.

Try additional problems. After practice, you will be able to use the abacus quickly and accurately.

AGRONOMY

Agronomy is a science that tries to improve the quality and quantity of plants grown as crops by farmers. Agronomists study many factors that affect plants: soil, nutrients, fertilizers, disease control, and pest control.

In this experiment, several different nutrients (foods) will be fed to several different plants of the same species. After the plants have been growing for a few weeks, you should be able to see which of the nutrients has had the best effect on a plant. You should also be able to tell which nutrient has had the most harmful effect.

Materials Needed: You will need 8 to 10 pots or plastic bowls, 30 to 40 seeds (bean seeds are good), sterilized potting soil, and several nutrient solutions. Why do you think you should use sterilized potting soil instead of soil from your garden or yard?

The nutrient solutions should be made from things you have around the house: water, milk, soda pop, orange juice, chlorine bleach, household ammonia, after-shave lotion, coffee, tea, and detergent. All of these solutions should be about room temperature when you feed them to the plants. Why do you think this is important?

You will also need masking tape to mark the pots, and paper for keeping a record of the results.

Procedure Fill each of the pots with the sterilized potting soil. Put 3 or 4 seeds in each of the pots, about ½ inch below the surface. Add enough plain water to each pot so that the soil is moist, but not soaking wet. Once the plants start growing, you will be feeding them every two or three days. It is important not to get the soil too wet. Why?

Put a piece of masking tape on each pot. On the masking tape, write the date, the number of the pot, and the nutrient that will be used. For example, on Pot 4 you will write something like this:

May 27   Pot #4   Soda Pop

Put all the pots on windowsills where they can get plenty of sunlight.

Using a separate sheet of paper for each of your plants, write down the headings as shown in the diagram. Keep these sheets in a safe place so they won't get wet when you feed the plants. Be sure that you have a sheet of paper for each of the pots. Also, check that each of the pots is marked with the date and nutrient to be used:

Pot #1: water
Pot #2: milk
Pot #3: orange juice
Pot #4: soda pop
Pot #5: chlorine bleach (mixed with water)
Pot #6: after-shave lotion (mixed with water)
Pot #7: household ammonia (mixed with water)
Pot #8: coffee
Pot #9: tea
Pot #10: detergent (mixed with water)

After a few days, the plants should have grown above the surface of the soil. When this happens, start using your nutrient solutions. Feed the plants every two or three days. Again, be careful not to feed them too much! Every time you feed the plants, write down the date on your result sheets. At this time, you should also write down your results. The results are the height (measure with a ruler), and the appearance, especially if something unusual happens—such as the leaves changing colors.

Conclusion After about five weeks, you can end the experiment. Using your result sheets as a guide, make a graph of your results. This graph will be a picture that will show you, at a glance, how the different nutrient solutions have affected the plants. Make your graph look like the one in the diagram. If you use different colors for each of the plants, it will be even easier to see how the plants compare with one another.

Try to answer these questions. Which plant is the tallest? Which is the shortest? Which is the healthiest? Is the tallest plant also the healthiest? Why did some plants seem to grow better than others? Did any of the plants die? If so, why?

Although this is a fairly simple experiment, it is similar to the kinds of experiments that agronomists do all the time. Based on your experiment, what are some of the things that help plants grow? If you were going to do an experiment like this again, what would you change?

PLANT #4	POTTING SOIL AND SODA POP	
DATE	HEIGHT	APPEARANCE

Make a separate page like this for each of your plants. When you measure the plants, be sure to write down the date as well as the height. Describe any changes you see under "appearance."

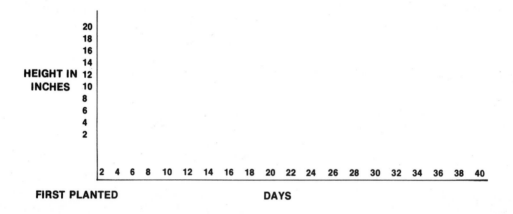

HEIGHT IN INCHES

FIRST PLANTED   **DAYS**

When the experiment is finished, make a graph to compare how the plants grew. Use a different color for each plant.

PROJECTS FOR VOLUME 2

ASEXUAL REPRODUCTION

Materials Needed:
three clear plastic cups
onion
African violet leaf
radish
toothpicks
rubber band
rooted cuttings

Procedure:
1. Fill three clear plastic cups with water.
2. Using toothpicks, support a root of a radish on top of a cup with the bottom of the root covered by water. See figure 2.
3. Repeat step 2 using toothpicks and onion.
4. Fold a piece of paper over the top of the third cup and fasten around the sides with a rubber band. Make a small hole in the paper that will allow the leaf stem (petiole) of the African violet to pass through and into the water, yet support the wide portion (blade) of the leaf.
5. Place all three cups in indirect light. Observe them daily until you see roots begin to grow in each type (root, stem, and leaf).

Keep a daily report of the root growth of the African violet leaf, onion, and radish root. Enter into your report such things as how the roots look, their size, where roots grow, length of roots, number of roots and other information you can find. Make sure you date each entry.

If you wish to continue, repeat this experiment using sand or soil instead of water.

This project shows a type of asexual reproduction. Most living things must reproduce using sexual means. In sexual reproduction, a male and a female are both needed. When a leaf is able to grow roots and form another plant, no sexual means have been used. Neither a male nor a female is needed.

BATTERY

Alessandro Volta, an Italian physicist, produced electricity by chemical reaction in 1800. He did this with a device that became known as a voltaic cell. It was the first wet cell battery. Volta's battery was made with pairs of zinc and silver pieces. The electric current ran from the zinc to the silver through pieces of board soaked in salt water. You can make your own simple voltaic cell.

Materials Needed:
piece of copper wire
fresh lemon
paper clip

Procedure:
1. Straighten out the paper clip and copper wire. They should be about the same length.
2. Thrust both wires deep into the lemon. They should be side by side, but not touching.
3. Put the free ends of the wires to your tongue. The slight tingle and metallic taste you feel is due to the passage of electrons through the saliva on your tongue. The acid in the lemon acted as an electrolyte. An electrolyte is a substance that is not metal that carries electricity. The chemical reaction caused electrons to build up on one of the wires and decrease on the other wire.

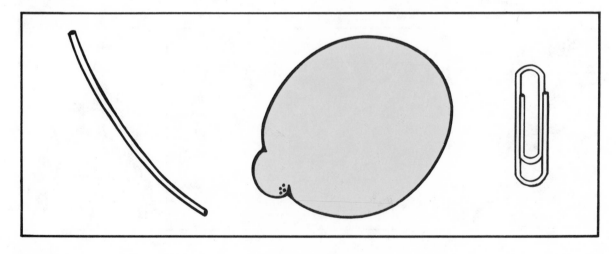

Conclusion:

When you put the free ends of the wires to your tongue, you closed the circuit between the two wires. Electrons flowed from the wire with more electrons, through your saliva that acted as a conductor, to the wire with fewer electrons. The entire system of lemon, wires, and saliva is a simple battery. It is similar to the first battery made by Alessandro Volta.

PROJECTS FOR VOLUME 3

CAMERA

How to Make a Pinhole Camera

The word camera comes from the Latin words "camera obscura," meaning dark chamber. You can make your own simple camera obscura, or pinhole camera, out of a dark box. This simple camera shows the basic principles of all more complex cameras.

Materials Needed:
small cardboard box
piece of wax paper
glue or tape
scissors
pin

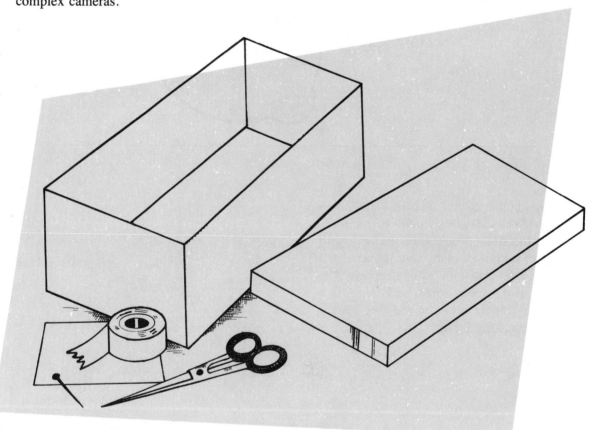

Procedure:
1. Cut a 5 cm [2 in] square hole in one end of the box.
2. Glue or tape the piece of wax paper over the hole.
3. Make a pinhole in the opposite end of the box that lines up with the center of the first hole.
4. Close the top of the box.
5. Point the end of the box containing the pinhole toward a well-lighted scene.
6. The image of the scene will appear upside-down on the wax paper.

An illustration of a completed pinhole camera is pictured above. To use the camera, the end of the closed box containing the pinhole is pointed toward a well-lighted scene. The image of the scene appears upside-down as in the illustration below.

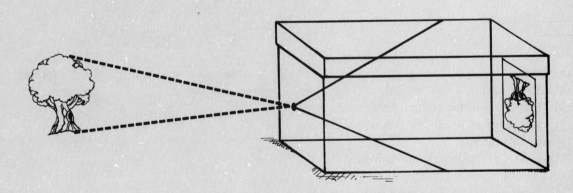

How the pinhole camera works is illustrated above. The end of the box containing the pinhole is pointed toward a tree. The image of the tree appears upside-down on the wax paper in the box. In some cameras, a mirror is used to turn the image right-side up.

CASTING

Police scientists often make a plaster cast of a footprint when a crime is being investigated. Scientists who study dinosaurs often make casts of footprints and fossils in order to learn more about them. With these materials you can make casts of footprints or twigs. If you like, you can make a cast of animal prints and try to find out what animal made them. You can find these prints in soft earth in a garden or in the woods. Try first with your own footprint.

Materials Needed:

wood or cardboard strips
plaster of Paris
modeling clay
measuring cup
mixing bowl
Vaseline
water

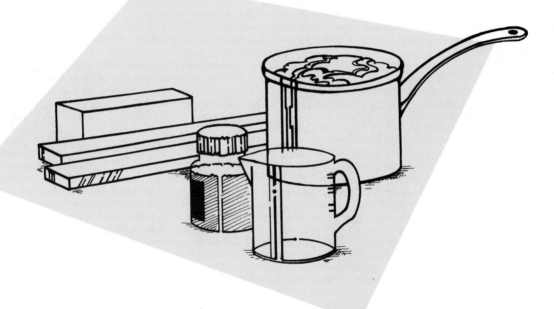

Procedure:
1. Make a footprint in soft ground.
2. Make a square frame around the footprint by pressing strips of wood or cardboard into the ground around it.
3. Make the frame watertight by sealing the joints with modeling clay.
4. Mix some plaster of Paris with water. Use 5 cupfuls of water to 2 cupfuls of plaster.
5. Quickly pour the solution over the footprint. In a few minutes the plaster will harden.
6. Remove the plaster when it has completely hardened. A clear cast of the footprint should remain.
7. Wash any dirt from the cast.
8. You can paint the cast to make the footprint stand out.

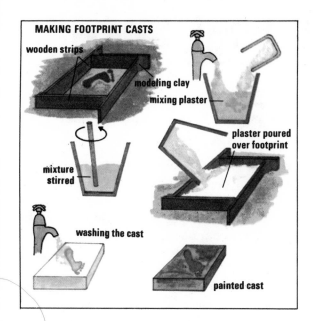

MAKING FOOTPRINT CASTS

wooden strips

modeling clay

mixing plaster

plaster poured over footprint

mixture stirred

washing the cast

painted cast

The procedure for casting footprints is illustrated at left. A square frame is placed around the footprint. The joints of the frame are sealed. A solution is mixed and poured over the footprint. The hardened cast is washed and painted.

To Make Plaster Casts of Twigs:

1. Take a large lump of modeling clay about the size of your fist and press it into a thin round disk about 2 cm [0.75 in] thick.
2. Cover the bottom of an aluminum pie pan with the clay disk.
3. Smear 2 or 3 small twigs with Vaseline.
4. Press the twigs into the clay.
5. Remove the twigs and pour plaster of Paris solution over the clay. When the plaster has hardened you will have a cast of the twigs.

PROJECT FOR VOLUME 4

COLOR

Mixing light of different colors sometimes produces surprising results. It is an entirely different process from mixing colored paints. For example, mixing red and green paints produces a dark brown color. But mixing red and green light produces yellow light. Mixing paints is an example of a process called color subtraction. Mixing colored light is an example of color addition.

White light is made up of colored light. When you look at a rainbow, you are seeing sunlight. The band of color in a rainbow is called a spectrum. The rainbow contains seven basic colors—red, orange, yellow, green, blue, indigo, and violet. Light of these colors can be recombined to form white light. You can even make white light from just three of these colors—red, green, and blue. These colors are primary colors of light.

Color television pictures are formed from light of three primary colors. Investigate the principles involved by experimenting with spinning, multicolored disks.

Materials Needed:
white cardboard
protractor
brushes
paint
pencil
glue

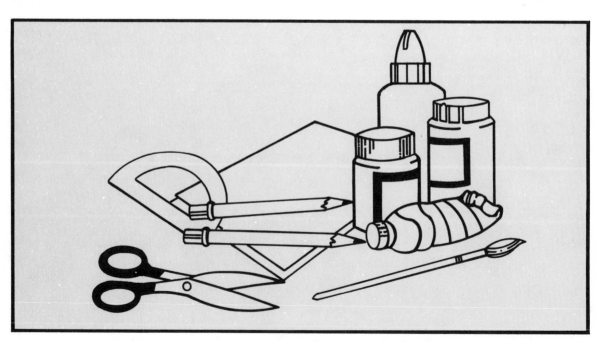

MIXING COLORED LIGHT

spectrum of colors present in white light

primary colors of light

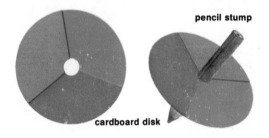

cardboard disk · pencil stump

the spinning colored disk
appears white

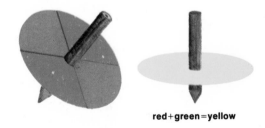

red+green=yellow

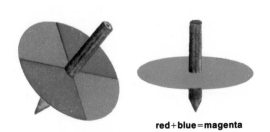

red+blue=magenta

Procedure:

1. Draw a circle about 7 cm [3 in] across on a piece of thick white cardboard.
2. Using a protractor, divide the circle into three equal sectors. The angles at the center of the disk should all be equal to 120°.
3. Paint one sector red, one green, and one blue.
4. Cut out the disk, and make a small hole through its center.
5. Push a pencil stump through the hole and glue or tape it in position, as shown in the diagram.
6. Flick the pencil to make the disk spin like a top. Light reflected from the three colored sectors appears to blend together. The disk looks white.
7. Try blending just red and green light. This time, divide the disk into four sectors by drawing lines through the center at right angles to each other.
8. Paint two sectors red and two green, as shown in the diagram.
9. Glue or tape the disk to a pencil as before. When the pencil is spun, the red and green disk should appear to be yellow.
10. Repeat the experiment using a four-sector disk painted red and blue. When combined by spinning the disk, these colors should form magenta (reddish purple).
11. Almost any color can be produced by mixing red, green, and blue light in various proportions. For example, try spinning a disk with two large red sectors and two small green sectors. The colors should combine to form orange. The shade of orange you get depends on the porportions of red and green that were used.
12. Spin a disk with four sectors colored red, blue, red, and green. We have already seen that equal proportions of red, blue, and green combine to form white. But in this case there is twice as much red as green or blue. The result is pink—in effect, a combination of white and red. Pink and other pale colors formed from white plus a color are usually called pastel colors.

⬛ PROJECTS FOR VOLUME 5

CONTOUR

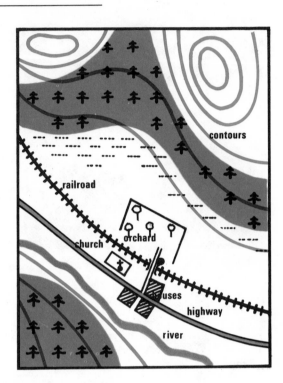

With the aid of a map showing land contours, you can make a realistic relief model of any area.

Procedure:

1. Find a map of the area you wish to model. Lay a sheet of tracing paper over the map and trace all the contours. (If you have a spare copy of the map, you can use this instead of tracing.)

2. Place carbon paper face down on a sheet of corrugated cardboard. Put the tracing paper over the carbon paper and retrace the lowest contour.

3. Move the tracing and carbon papers to a fresh area of the cardboard and trace out the next highest contour.

4. Repeat the process until you have transferred tracings of all the contours to separate parts of the cardboard.

5. Cut around the contours on the cardboard.

6. Stick the map tracing onto a sheet of thick cardboard.

7. On top of the map tracing, stick down the cardboard shapes corresponding to the lowest contours.

8. Using the original map as a guide, build up the model by sticking down the other cardboard shapes in order of their contour heights. When you have finished, hillsides on the model will be rough and have "steps" from one contour to the next.

9. Paste strips of newspaper over the model to form smooth slopes between the contours.

10. Leave the model in a warm place to dry.

11. Paint the model to show the various features on the original map. Houses and other constructions can be made to scale from scraps of balsa.

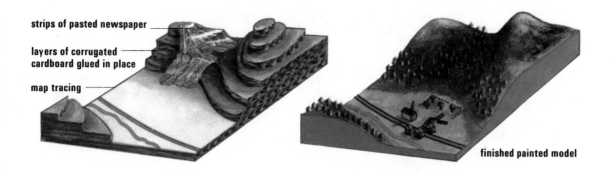

strips of pasted newspaper

layers of corrugated cardboard glued in place

map tracing

finished painted model

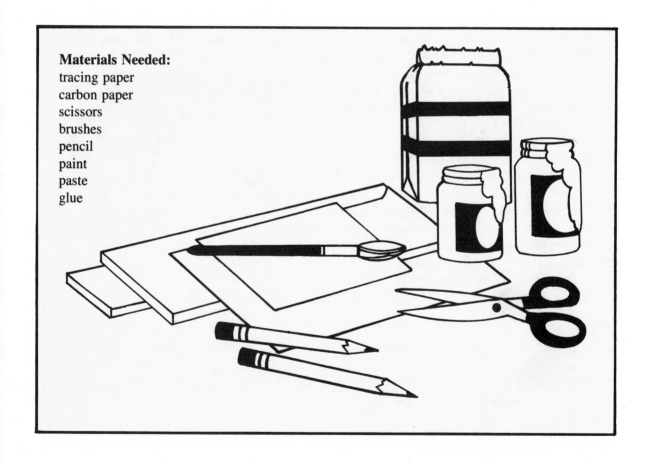

Materials Needed:
tracing paper
carbon paper
scissors
brushes
pencil
paint
paste
glue

CRYSTALS

With simple equipment, you can grow large, beautiful crystals. You can also grow strange, feathery crystalline structures in a chemical garden.

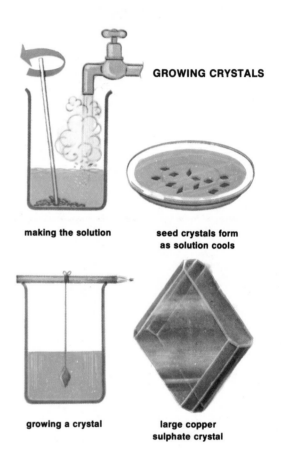

GROWING CRYSTALS

making the solution

seed crystals form
as solution cools

growing a crystal

large copper
sulphate crystal

Procedure:
1. Add crystals of copper sulfate to some hot water in a jar. Stir until no more crystals will dissolve.
2. Pour a little of the solution into a saucer and allow it to cool. After several hours, you should see small crystals in the saucer.
3. Select a few well-formed crystals. These will be used as "seed" crystals for growing.
4. Take the jar of copper sulfate solution and pour off the liquid into another jar, leaving behind any crystals that have formed.
5. Tie a fine thread around one of the seed crystals. (Keep the other seed crystals in case your first attempt at crystal growing is not successful.)
6. Hang the crystal in the copper sulfate solution. Leave the crystal undisturbed for several days. As the water evaporates from the solution, copper sulfate will be deposited onto the seed crystal, causing it to grow. For best results, reduce the rate of evaporation by covering the top of the jar with paper.
7. Let the crystal grow for several weeks. From time to time, remove any other crystals that form.
8. Try growing crystals of other substances—for example, alum, copper acetate, sodium nitrate, and nickel sulfate. Some chemicals are poisonous, so always wash the apparatus and your hands after experimenting.

Making a Chemical Garden

1. Mix equal volumes of water and water glass.
2. Pour this solution into a glass tank and drop in crystals of various chemicals. Attractive crystalline growths will form as the chemicals react with the solution. Crystals of common alum produce growths within a few minutes. Most other chemicals take much longer.

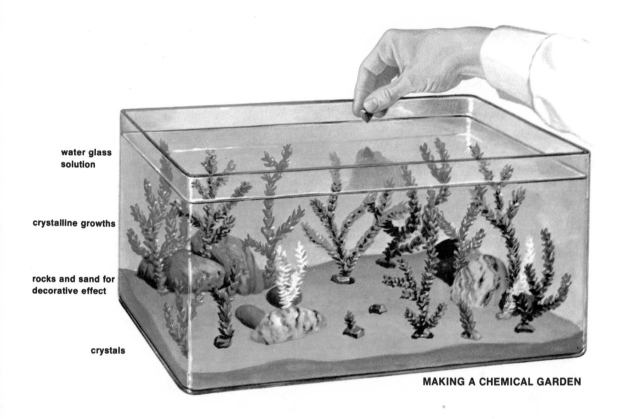

water glass
solution

crystalline growths

rocks and sand for
decorative effect

crystals

MAKING A CHEMICAL GARDEN

PROJECTS FOR VOLUME 6

DISTILLATION

Making fresh water from salt water is a good example of simple distillation. This method of distilling water has been used for centuries. Sailors on the ocean used this method of evaporation to make drinking water from seawater. Modern salt evaporators use the same principle today in industry.

Materials Needed:

flat rectangular tray
Wooden board a little larger than the tray
aluminum foil
black enamel paint
large transparent plastic food bags
paint brush
stiff wire
tape
cup
seawater or salt and water
scissors

Procedure:

1. Cover the top of the board with aluminum foil. Shape the foil all the way around the edge of the board so that you make a trough to carry water in. In one corner of the foil make an outlet for the trough so that the water can run out there.
2. Paint the inside of the tray black. Let it dry. Put the tray on the aluminum-covered board inside the trough.
3. Fill the tray halfway with seawater or salty fresh water.
4. Bend the wire into a triangular shape as shown in the picture. Make it so that it will fit just outside the aluminum trough.
5. Cut the plastic into sheets. Using the tape, cover the outside of the wire shape with the plastic. Make sure the plastic is fairly tight. Do not rip it.
6. Place the plastic and wire tent around the outside edge of the trough. Put the whole model in strong sunlight or a few feet beneath a heat lamp. Put a cup under the outlet from the trough. Tilt the board a little to help water run down to the outlet.
7. When some water has collected in the cup, taste it. It should be fresh water.

The sun's rays passed through the plastic and were absorbed by the black tray. The tray became hot and heated the salt water. Some of the water then evaporated and became water vapor. The water vapor rose to the plastic and condensed there, forming water droplets. That water ran down the plastic and into the trough. Since pure water evaporates at a much lower temperature than salt, the water evaporated and left the salt behind.

DYE

Attractive, brilliant patterns can be produced by a method called tie dyeing. Japanese garments called kimonos are sometimes colored by dyes in this way. Use the technique to make a variety of designs on white cotton materials as these do not readily absorb dyes. Cold-water dye can be purchased in supermarkets.

Materials needed:
cloth
scissors
stones
string
dyes
pans

Procedure:
1. Clean the cotton material by washing it in soap or detergent. Rinse well and allow to dry.

2. Place stones in the material. Gather the cloth around the stones and bind it with string in several places.
3. Dye the tied material in blue cold-water dye, following the instruction on the packet.
4. After dyeing, rinse well, remove the string, and hang the material out to dry. It should display circles of blue separated by white areas where the material was bound with string.
5. Put the stones back in the cloth when it is dry. Rebind the material in different places than you did the first time.
6. Soak the bound material in yellow dye. After rinsing, remove the string and dry the material. Where it was protected by binding during both dyeing processes, it will still be white. It will be yellow in the places where only the yellow dye has colored it and blue where only the blue dye has colored it. In other places,

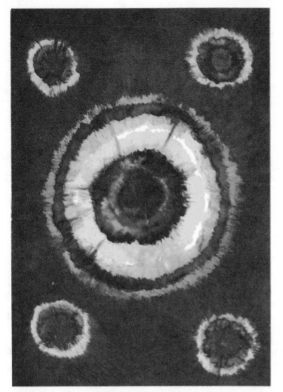

typical tie-dyed patterns

where both dyes have colored it, the material will be green. Circular patterns will be formed around the positions where the stones were bound into the material.

Similar patterns can be made by using other color combinations such as blue and red or red and yellow. It is best to use primary colors as these will form a third color in places where both dyes affect the material. Whenever using combinations of colors, always dye the material with the strongest color first. For example, use red before blue, and use blue before yellow.

MAKING TIE-DYED PATTERNS

after blue dyeing

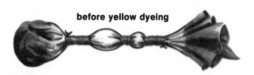

before yellow dyeing

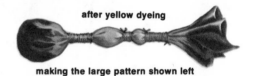

after yellow dyeing

making the large pattern shown left

ELECTRIC BELL

In 1819, Hans Oersted found that an electric current passing through a wire produces a magnetic field. The principle of electromagnetism had been discovered. The importance of this discovery can be judged by the fact that transformers, loudspeakers, electric motors, electric bells, and many other electrical devices work on the principle of electromagnetism.

In the electric bell, a current from a battery passes through a small electromagnet and attracts an iron strip. The movement of the iron toward the electromagnet cuts off the current. As a result, the electromagnet no longer attracts the iron. The iron springs back to its original position and reconnects the battery to the electromagnet. The process repeats itself and causes the iron bar to vibrate continuously. A "strike," attached to the iron strip hits a bell gong, making it ring.

An ambitious experimenter can make an electric bell of this type from readily available materials. The dimensions can vary depending on what materials are easily available. You can use the electric bell as part of a fire alarm system by connecting it to a home-made thermostat that incorporates a bimetallic strip.

Procedure:
1. To make the electromagnet, cut out two cardboard washers, diameter 2 cm [0.75 in]. Glue them around an iron rod, 4 cm [1.5 in] long and 1 cm [0.4 in] in diameter.
2. Next, wind enameled copper wire evenly around the iron rod to form a coil, as shown in the diagram. The ends of the wire can be anchored by passing them through holes in the cardboard washer. They can also be fixed in position with sticky tape.
3. Glue the protruding end of the electromagnet in a hole you have made in a small wooden block.
4. Test the electromagnet by connecting the ends of the wire to a 4-5 volt or 6-volt bell battery.

You must first scrape away the enamel insulation covering the ends of the wire. With the battery connected, the electromagnet should attract nearby pieces of iron or steel.
5. To make the bell gong, drill a hole through the center of a tin lid. Insert a wood screw through the hole and screw the lid to the wooden base of the electric bell. Thread some washers onto the screw so that they separate the lid from the wood. This arrangement will allow the lid to vibrate freely and noisily when struck.
6. Now make the armature (the movable part of the electric bell) from strips of spring steel and iron. Drill the strips as shown and bend them to shape.
7. Bolt the strips together and fix a large bolt and nut through the end of the iron. The bolt acts as the bell clapper.
8. Screw the spring to a wooden supporting block and fix one end of the coil underneath one of the screw heads.
9. Glue or screw the blocks supporting the armature and electromagnet to the wooden base board. Position the blocks so that the bell clapper is about 5 cm [2 in] from the gong. Be sure that the end of the electromagnet is about the same distance from the armature.
10. Screw a small metal bracket onto the baseboard opposite the armature spring. Trap one end of a few centimeters of wire under one of the screw heads.
11. Drill a hole through the upright part of the bracket. Fix a bolt through the hole (as shown) using two nuts, one on either side of the bracket. The end of the bolt should push slightly against the spring in order to make a good electrical connection. For best results, file the end of this bolt to a point.
12. Push the armature toward the gong. Check that the spring breaks contact with the bolt just before the clapper touches the gong. If necessary, adjust the position of the bolt.

22

13. Make the connecting terminals by passing two large bolts through the baseboard. Around one bolt, wrap the other end of the wire from the bracket. Around the second bolt, wrap the remaining wire from the electromagnet. Then place washers over the bolts and clamp the wires securely in place with nuts. The electric bell is now complete.

14. Connect the bell to a push-button switch and a bell battery. (See diagram.) Pressing the button should make the bell ring. If it does not, check all connections and try adjusting the position of the contact bolt. When it is operating satisfactorily, the bell can be connected to a push-button switch fixed to your front door.

MAKING AN ELECTRIC BELL

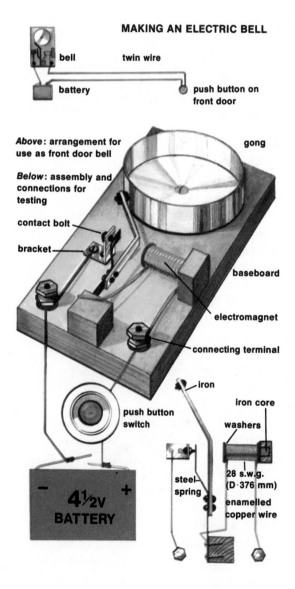

bell

twin wire

battery

push button on front door

Above: arrangement for use as front door bell

gong

Below: assembly and connections for testing

contact bolt

bracket

baseboard

electromagnet

connecting terminal

iron

iron core

washers

push button switch

steel spring

28 s.w.g. (D·376 mm) enamelled copper wire

4½V BATTERY

PROJECT FOR VOLUME 7

EXTRASENSORY PERCEPTION

Can you tell what people are thinking or doing when you cannot see or hear them? Many people claim to have this power. Some also claim to be able to send information to others without using any known means of communication. These strange powers of thought transference are called telepathy. It is a form of extrasensory perception, or ESP—the ability to become aware of thoughts or events without using the known senses.

Clairvoyance is similar to telepathy, except that thought-transference is not involved. A person is said to be clairvoyant when he or she knows about an event without using the known senses and without anyone trying to send information by telepathy.

Do you possess extrasensory perception? Are you telepathic or clairvoyant? Find out by performing the following tests.

Procedure:
1. Cut 25 rectangles about the size of ordinary playing cards from a sheet of cardboard.
2. Mark one side of each card with a star, square, circle, cross, or wave. Each symbol should be marked on five cards.
3. Mark the five symbols on a large sheet of paper.
4. Shuffle the cards, then take the top one. Look at it, but do not let anyone but yourself see it. Ask a friend to guess the symbol on the card you have chosen. Place the card face down on the paper next to the symbol he or she has guessed.
5. Take the next card, and do the same again. Continue with the rest of the cards.
6. When all the cards have been used, turn up the cards and count how many guesses were correct. An average of five guesses should be correct—assuming that no powers of extrasen-sory perception were used. If more than five are correct, then you may have sent information to your friend by telepathy. Or, of course, your friend may just have been lucky in his or her guessing. So repeat the experiment many times and see whether, on the average, more than one-fifth of the guesses are correct.
7. The test for clairvoyance is similar to the test for telepathy. The only difference is that when you take a card from the pack, you do not look at it. The other person has to guess the symbol on the card before anyone sees it.

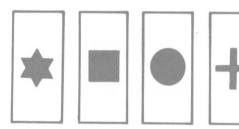

Cards used for ESP tests. The complete set consists of 25 cards, 5 of each kind.

PROJECTS FOR VOLUME 8

FISH

Some fishes make nests in which to lay their eggs. Others take their babies into their mouths for protection if danger appears. These are some of the fascinating things you can watch if you set up an aquarium and stock it with a few fishes.

You can use any watertight container as an aquarium. But it is best to use a container with transparent sides. This makes it easier to observe the fishes' activities. A large jar can be used if you do not intend to keep more than a couple of small fishes, but a properly made aquarium is better. It is important that the aquarium should have a large surface area. The fishes depend on oxygen dissolved in the water. Most of this oxygen comes from the air and enters the water through the surface.

Procedure:

1. Collect some sand or gravel and wash it in a bowl. Stir continuously while running cold water into the bowl.
2. When the water is no longer cloudy, put about 3 cm [1 in] of the clean material in the bottom of the aquarium.
3. Fill up the tank after putting it in the place you wish to keep it. You may find it too heavy to carry if you fill it up first. Put the tank in a place that is reasonably light. Do not put it in a window. Bright light causes little plants called algae to grow in the water. They can soon coat the sides of the tank and prevent you from seeing the fishes. Use pond water or rainwater in preference to tap water. If you do use tap water, boil it first to remove any chlorine in it. To prevent disturbance of the sand, pour the water onto a saucer placed on the bottom of the tank.
4. If you are going to get fishes from a local pond or stream, collect a few water plants, too. If you are going to buy fishes from a pet store, you can also buy the plants there. Push the plants into the sand or gravel and hold them in place with small stones.
5. A few small water snails or pond mussels will help to keep the water and the sides of the tank clear by eating any algae that start to grow.

AN AQUARIUM FOR TROPICAL FISH

cover prevents
fish jumping out

thermostat
regulates
temperature

water plants
provide oxygen

water heater

gravel

Keeping Guppies

One of the easiest fish to keep in the aquarium is the common guppy. A native of various Caribbean islands, the guppy is readily obtainable from pet stores. Many varieties are available. They are no more than about 5 cm [2 in] long, and six of them can be kept quite easily in a tank measuring about 30 cm × 15 cm × 15 cm [12 in × 6 in × 6 in]. Guppies tolerate a wide range of temperatures and no heating is needed in summer. During winter, a small electric light placed beside the tank should keep the fish warm enough. Feed them on water fleas and other small creatures that can be caught in a pond.

Watch the fascinating courtship dances of the brightly colored male as he floats in front of the fatter, duller female and vibrates his long fins. Later on, you may see the female giving birth to her tiny babies and then turning around immediately to eat them. She usually succeeds unless there are plenty of weeds in which the young fish can hide. If you want to breed guppies, you will have to trap the mother in a net when she starts to give birth. The net can be made from a piece of old stocking fastened to a wire frame. A square frame is best as this fits into the corners of the tank better than a round one. Make a few small holes in the net so that the young guppies can escape. They can then be caught in a net without holes and transferred to a jar. Keep them away from the mother until they are too big for her to eat.

Feeding Your Fishes

If you cannot get living food for your fishes, you can use one of the dried foods sold in pet shops. Never give too much at a time. The fish will not eat more than they need. Excess food will decay and make the aquarium smell. A feeding ring on the surface of the water will help to keep the food in one part of the tank. This simple device makes it easy to remove any decaying food that may collect. A properly set up aquarium should not need cleaning out very often because the plants use up the animals' waste products and keep the water fresh.

SOME SPECIES OF GOLDFISH

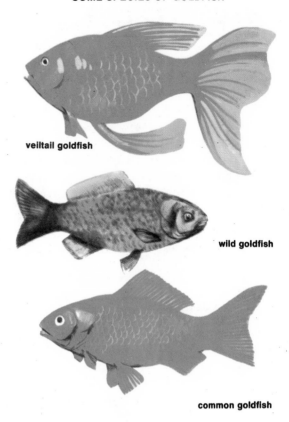

veiltail goldfish

wild goldfish

common goldfish

GENERATOR, ELECTRIC

Electric generators produce most of our electricity. The largest generators supply cities with millions of watts of power. Small generators used on bicycles supply about two watts to the front and rear lights. But both types of generator work on the same principle. Electricity is produced in a wire when it is cut by lines of magnetic force. In the generator described here, a permanent magnet rotates near fixed coils of wire. As the magnet's lines of force pass through the coils, electricity is generated in the coils.

Procedure:

1. Obtain a strong, U-shaped magnet. A large magnet is best.
2. Cut out wood or plastic mounting blocks to fit the magnet, and glue them in place. (See diagram.)
3. Make the coils by winding 28 s.w.g. [0.376 mm diameter] enameled copper wire around iron rods, about 5 cm [2 in] long. Square or round rods will do. They should be about equal in thickness to the poles of the magnet. Glue

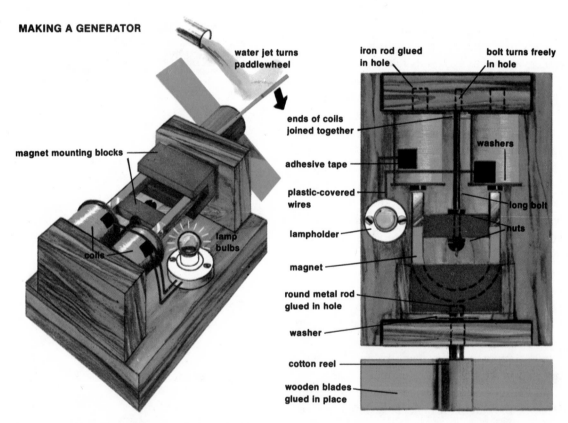

MAKING A GENERATOR

water jet turns paddlewheel

magnet mounting blocks

coils

lamp bulbs

iron rod glued in hole

bolt turns freely in hole

ends of coils joined together

adhesive tape

plastic-covered wires

lampholder

magnet

round metal rod glued in hole

washer

cotton reel

wooden blades glued in place

washers

long bolt

nuts

The energy of moving water is transferred to the paddle wheel, which turns the shaft to which a horseshoe magnet is attached. As its magnetic field moves, an electric current flows in the coils.

Top view of the generator at the left. Note the connection of the light bulb to the coils. The electric current generated flows from the coils through the light bulb and back again.

cardboard washers to the rods, as shown. They will keep the windings from slipping off. Wind as many turns on the coils as possible, bearing the following points in mind. In the finished generator, the distance between coil centers will be equal to the distance between the poles of the magnet. There must be room between the coils for a thick spindle. These two factors determine the maximum possible diameter of the coils.

4. Glue the protruding ends of the iron rods into holes in a wooden block. Make the distance between the holes equal to the distance between the magnet's poles. The height of the holes above the base of the block should be at least half this distance.

5. Connect the end of one coil to the end of the other coil. Remember to scrape the insulation from the wires to ensure good electrical contact. With two lengths of fine, flexible, plastic-covered wire connect the other ends of the coils to a miniature lampholder mounted on a baseboard.

6. Mount the magnet as shown in the diagram. It should turn freely. The poles should just clear the iron rods.

Operating the Generator

If you fit a paddle wheel to the magnet shaft, you can use a water jet to turn the generator. (See diagram.) Or else you can connect the drive shaft of a large clockwork motor to the magnet shaft. Whatever system you use to drive the generator, try to make it turn as fast as possible. The quicker it turns, the greater will be the generated voltage. This voltage will depend also on the number of turns on the coils.

Screw a 2.5-volt light bulb into the lampholder. Then make the generator turn at a gradually increasing speed. If the light bulb does not light, even at maximum speed, reverse the connections to one coil and try again. The voltages induced in each coil will either add together or cancel, depending on the way the coils are connected. If the lamp glows extremely brightly at any stage, replace it with a lamp of higher voltage rating. Otherwise, it may soon burn out.

◤PROJECTS FOR VOLUME 9

PROJECT

GERMINATION

The seed of a redwood tree is no larger than a pin's head. Yet it can grow into a giant tree nearly 400 feet [120 m] tall and weigh more than 1,000 tons. Have you ever wondered how a seed begins to grow into a mature plant? The early stages of its growth are called germination. It is easy to study germination at home. Redwood seeds are too small for this purpose. But peas and beans are ideal. They are quite large and their germination is essentially the same as those of any other seed.

Procedure:

1. All you need, apart from the seeds, are a few jam jars and some blotting paper. Line the jars with the blotting paper and push a few seeds down between the glass and the paper in each jar. Moisten the blotting paper thoroughly in one jar and keep it in a warm room. Make sure that the paper remains moist. But do not have a lot of free water running about in the bottom of the jar.

2. You will soon notice the seeds beginning to swell as they absorb water. The seed coat will burst after a day or two and a little root will appear. Notice that no matter how the seed has been ''planted,'' the root always bends downward. This is essential for the health of the young plant because the root has to anchor it in the ground. After another day or two, you will see a fluffy mass near the tip of the root. This is made up of thousands of tiny root hairs. They help the root to absorb water.

A shoot will emerge from the seed and grow upward. It carries the leaves. These are creamy yellow at first. Only when they have been exposed to the light for a few hours do they turn green. This is because the green pigment called chlorophyll can be made only in light.

BEAN GERMINATION EXPERIMENT

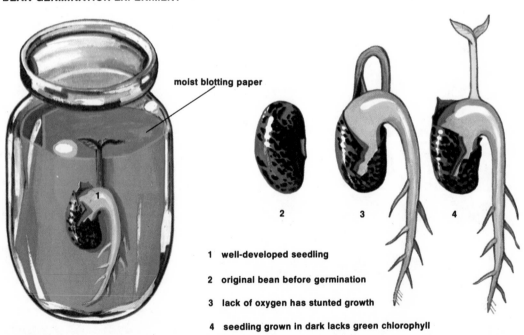

moist blotting paper

1 well-developed seedling

2 original bean before germination

3 lack of oxygen has stunted growth

4 seedling grown in dark lacks green chlorophyll

Up until this time, the seedling has existed on food reserves in the seed. You will notice that the seed shrivels as these reserves are used up. As soon as the leaves become green, however, they can make food by photosynthesis. The plant is no longer dependent on the seed's reserves. Germination is at an end. Add some soil to the jar now. Watch the further growth of the seedling and the development of branch roots. Then plant the seedlings in your garden. You can now study the development of the flowers and fruits.

The other jars lined with blotting paper can be used to find out what conditions are necessary for germination. Moisten two more, exactly as you did before. Put one in a refrigerator and the other in a warm, dark cupboard. Remember to keep the paper moist. Leave a third jar dry. Keep it warm. Put a piece of steel wool into a fourth jar and moisten it thoroughly. Then seal the top securely. Keep the jar warm.

Examine the jars in a few days. You will find that the dry seeds and those in the refrigerator have not started to grow. This shows that seeds need warmth and moisture if they are to germinate. The seeds with the iron filings will have grown a little. The filings will have rusted and they will have used up the oxygen in the jar. The lack of oxygen prevents further growth. The seedlings kept in the dark will have grown well. This shows that they do not need light to germinate although some kinds of seeds do. The seedlings will not be green. If you put them in the light now, they will soon become green. If you keep them in the dark, however, they will not be able to make food and they will die.

HELIOGRAPHY

Heliographs are signalling devices that use reflected sunlight. They provided rapid communication between towns in 11th century Algeria. In the 1800s, heliography became a popular means of communication between army units on the battlefield. Build the heliograph described below, and practice sending Morse code messages to your friends.

Procedure:

1. Glue wooden backing blocks to small mirrors. Screw them to brackets made by bending metal strips. One bracket should be about twice as long as the other.
2. Screw the brackets to a wooden baseboard. Screw two wooden strips to the front of the baseboard. These will support the shutter mechanism. (See diagram.)
3. Make the shutter mechanism from two pieces of thin wood. Cut three large identical slots in both pieces of wood. These slots should be the same size as the bars between the slots.
4. Make four small slots in one part of the shutter. This part will serve as the moving front of the mechanism. Pass wood screws through the slots. Screw them through the back of the shutter and into the two wooden strips. The screw heads must be a little larger than the width of the slots. The screws must be loose enough to allow the shutter front to slide smoothly up and down. Position the screws so that in the up position, the front of the shutter

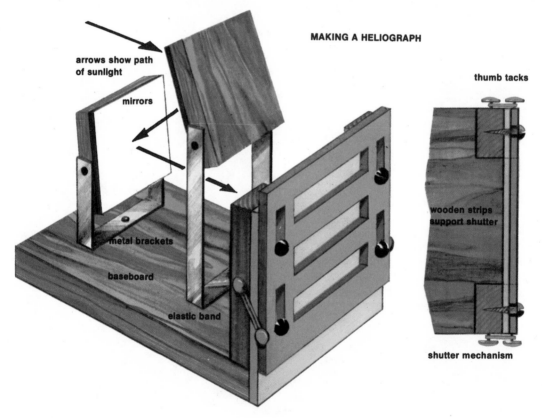

arrows show path of sunlight

mirrors

MAKING A HELIOGRAPH

thumb tacks

metal brackets

baseboard

elastic band

wooden strips support shutter

shutter mechanism

obscures the large slots behind. In the down position, these slots should be fully exposed.

5. Fasten four thumbtacks and two small elastic bands to the shutter mechanism. (See diagram.) With this arrangement, the shutter is normally held in the closed position.

Operation

Point the heliograph in the direction you wish to send signals. If sunlight is coming from the front, let it fall directly on the back mirror. In this case, the front mirror is not used. Adjust the angle of the back mirror so that sunlight is reflected onto the back of the shutter. Flashes of light can then be sent by pressing and releasing the shutter.

If the sun is behind you, arrange the mirrors so that light is reflected from the front mirror onto the back one. Then proceed as described above.

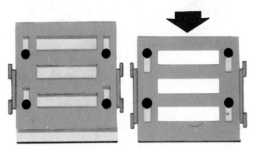

heliograph shutter closed (left), and open (right)

PROJECT FOR VOLUME 10
HUMIDITY

We often complain that a room feels uncomfortably hot or cold. But it is not always the room temperature that is too high or low. Air flow and humidity—the amount of moisture in the air—also affect our comfort. Build the hair hygrometer described below and use it to investigate how humidity variation affects your comfort.

Procedure:

1. Soak a hair in detergent and then rinse it in water to remove natural oils.
2. Nail one nail into each end of a square wood block about 7.5 cm by 10 cm [3 in by 4 in] wide.
3. Carefully tie one end of the hair to a rubber band. Twist the rubber band and attach it to one nail.
4. Attach a square piece of cardboard to one end of the block and glue a smaller block on the front of the larger one as shown in the diagram.
5. Pin a wooden cylinder between the small block and the cardboard.
6. Split the end of a drinking straw and glue it to the wooden cylinder as shown.
7. Wrap the hair once around the wooden cylinder and attach the other end to the other nail.
8. Mark a scale on the cardboard as shown.

Check to be sure that the hygrometer is working by placing it near a steaming kettle. The moisture should make the hair stretch and should cause the pointer to turn to the high end of the scale. The instrument will respond quite well to slow, day-to-day humidity changes. But it will take a long time to recover after being exposed to steam.

Adjust the position of the pointer by trial and error until, over long periods, its average position is at the center of the scale. You will then be able to see, at a glance, whether the humidity is above or below its normal level in your house.

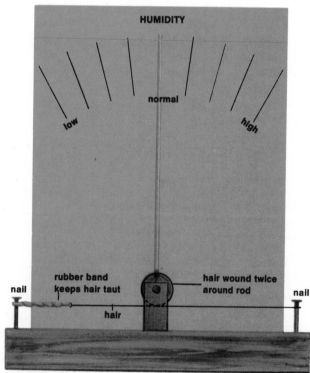

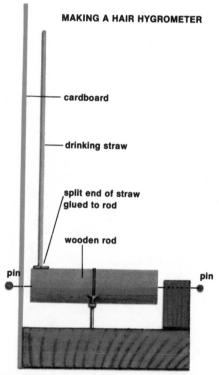

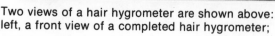

Two views of a hair hygrometer are shown above: left, a front view of a completed hair hygrometer; right, a side view showing placement of the different parts of the hair hygrometer.

PROJECTS FOR VOLUME 11

JET PROPULSION

Jet propulsion is used by sea animals such as squids. They squirt out a jet of water in one direction in order to move in the opposite direction. The same principle is used in jets and rockets.

In the jet-propelled boat described below, high-pressure air streams out of the balloon in one direction. This makes the boat move in the opposite direction through the water.

Materials Needed:
block of balsa wood
thin cardboard box (heavy paper will also work)
oil-base model paint
long balloon
glue

Procedure:
1. Carve a simple boat from the balsa wood. The boat should be about 15 by 35 cm [6 by 14 in]. Paint the boat.
2. Cut one panel out of the cardboard box. (See diagram.) Glue the box to the deck of the boat.
3. Blow up the balloon, making sure that it is not too wide to fit into the box. It is all right if the balloon extends several inches beyond the back of the boat.
4. Holding the opening of the blown-up balloon, set it into the box. When you let go of the balloon, the air shooting out will push the boat forward through the water.

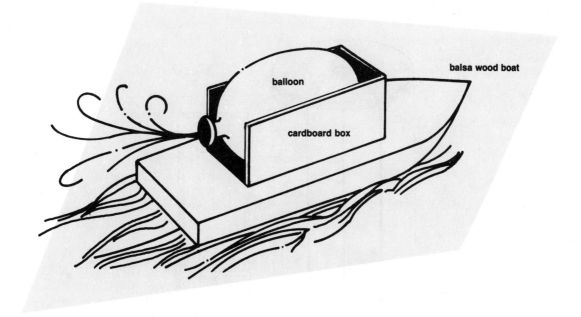

KALEIDOSCOPE

With a kaleidoscope, you can produce beautiful colored patterns. In the instrument described below, two mirrors form many images of the pieces of colored material.

Procedure:
1. Obtain a round cardboard tube that is about 20 cm [8 in] long and about 5 cm [2 in] in diameter.
2. Get two strips of polished aluminum from a hardware store. These will be used as mirrors.

Each strip should be about as long as the tube. The width of each strip should be just a little bit less than the diameter of the tube. To be exact, it should be 0.95 times the diameter. Push the mirrors into the tube so that they are at a 36° angle to each other. Check the angle with a protractor. Use cellophane tape to attach the backs of the mirrors to the tube. Remember, the mirrors should be touching each other along one edge.

3. Complete the kaleidoscope by making and attaching the end pieces. Cut out a small eyehole in the middle of the front end. At the back end, place many small pieces of colored glass or plastic between two disks of plastic. The inner disk should be clear. The outer disk should be translucent, like wax paper. It has to be able to let light through.
4. Point the back end of your kaleidoscope to-

MAKING A KALEIDOSCOPE

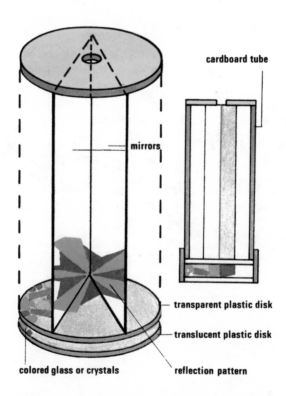

cardboard tube

mirrors

transparent plastic disk

translucent plastic disk

colored glass or crystals

reflection pattern

ward a light bulb and look through the eyehole you cut in the front end. You may have to move the mirrors a little in order to get a regular pattern. Once you have found the best angle for the mirrors, glue them in place. After the glue has dried, look through the kaleidoscope again. This time, turn it slowly and watch what happens!

typical kaleidoscope patterns

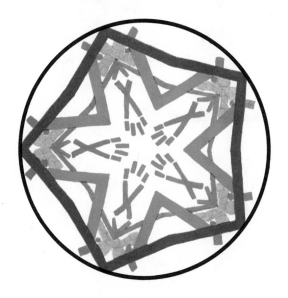

◤ PROJECTS FOR VOLUME 12

SIMPLE MACHINE

"Give me a place to stand on, and I will move the earth." Thus spoke Archimedes, the Greek mathematician, astronomer, and inventor. Archimedes meant that by using simple machines such as levers or pulleys, he could move any object.

Experiment with the pulley systems described in this project and see how a small force can move a heavy object.

Materials needed:
glue
wooden rod
disks
blocks
metal strip
screws
metal "eye"

Procedure:
1. Make four pulley wheels by glueing together disks cut from round wooden rods. (See diagram.) Complete the pulleys by fixing metal strips and wooden blocks to the wheels, as shown.
2. Suspend one pulley from any convenient support. (Diagram A.) Try hoisting a weight (load) on a string passing over the pulley. The force (effort) with which the string must be pulled is about the same as the force required to lift the weight when no pulley system is used.
3. Set up the pulley system shown in diagram B. Using the same effort as before, it is possible to lift about twice the load. But for each meter

EXPERIMENTS WITH PULLEYS

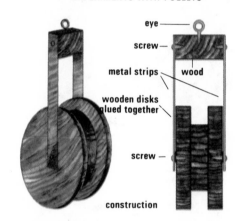

eye

screw

metal strips   wood

wooden disks glued together

screw

construction

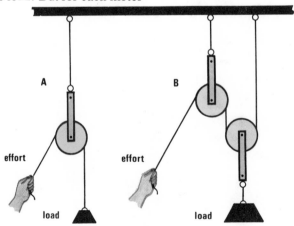

A

effort

load

B

effort

load

or yard you raise the weight, you have to pull the string two meters or yards.

4. Set up the pulley system shown in diagram C. Using the same effort again, it is possible to raise about four times the original load. In this case, you have to pull the string four meters or yards to raise the load one meter or yard.

Conclusion

Pulley systems allow us to raise heavy loads with much less effort. But such systems do not reduce the amount of work that has to be done. For instance, in experiment C, the effort is about the same as in experiment A. But the distance the string must be pulled is four times as great. So the work (force times distance) that is done on the load is the same in both cases. The total work done in experiment C is, in fact, greater than the total work done in experiment A. Besides raising the weight, some work must be done to raise the pulleys and turn them against forces of friction.

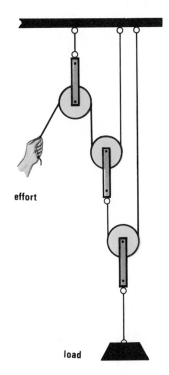

PULLEY
EXPERIMENT
C

effort

load

MAGNETISM

The exact nature of magnetic forces has always been a mystery. But some of the effects these strange forces have can be studied.

Displaying a Magnetic Field

Procedure:
1. Place a large sheet of cardboard over a bar magnet.

2. Sprinkle iron filings on the cardboard.
3. Gently tap the cardboard. It can be seen that the filings arrange themselves along the lines of force of the magnet's field. (See diagram.)

EXPERIMENTS WITH MAGNETS

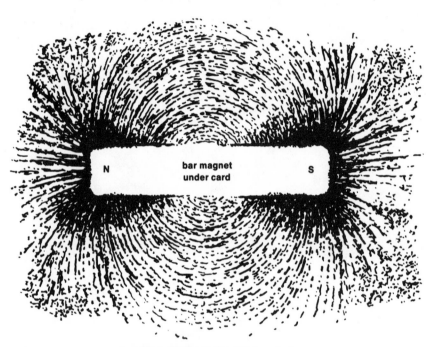

iron filings display field around magnet

Plotting Magnetic Fields

1. Obtain two bar magnets. Glue the north pole of one magnet and the south pole of the other magnet under a sheet of cardboard. The distance between the poles should be about 30 cm [1 ft].
2. Place a magnetic compass on top of the cardboard and between the poles of the magnet. The needle of the compass turns to point along a line of force.

3. Mark the cardboard with a dot near each end of the needle to record the needle position.
4. Move the compass along until its south pole points to the dot that was first near its north pole. Mark the new position of the north pole.
5. Continue plotting points in this way to form complete lines of dots between the magnets. Then join the dots with smooth, curved lines. These represent the lines of magnetic force.

6. Repeat the procedure, but with a piece of iron between the poles of the magnets. (See diagram.) Notice how the compass direction changes near the iron, showing that the iron has distorted the magnetic field. Remember this experiment when using a compass for finding direction. Always keep well away from iron and steel objects. If this is not done, the compass readings will be wrong.

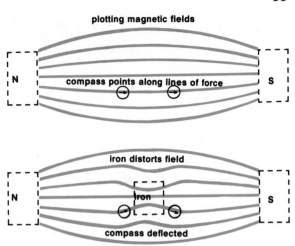

plotting magnetic fields

compass points along lines of force

N   S

iron distorts field

Iron

N   S

compass deflected

PROJECTS FOR VOLUME 13

MIRROR

The device described below makes it possible for you to see through solid objects! Not really—it just seems that way. Actually, you see around the object. But the device contains mirrors that make you think that you are seeing through the object.

Materials Needed:
4 mirrors about 5 cm [2 in] square
box the same height as the mirrors
ruler
glue

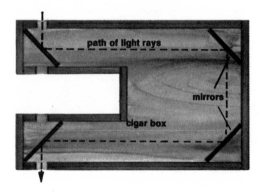

Procedure:
1. Cut out a large slot in one end of the box. Block the sides of the slot, using scraps you have cut out. (See diagram.)
2. Place the mirrors in the corners of the box as shown in the diagram.
3. On the box, mark the mirror positions. Make sure that each is at 45° to the sides of the box. Then remove the mirrors and cut four holes, diameter 5 mm [0.2 in], through the box, as shown in the diagram. The holes should be in line with the centers of the mirrors opposite them.
4. Glue the mirrors in place and check to be sure they are positioned correctly. If they are, it should be possible to look through the hole in one side of the box and, apparently, to see straight through it. Actually, light from distant objects viewed through the box travels around the box, following the path shown in the diagram.
5. When the mirrors have been correctly positioned, glue down the lid of the box. The apparatus is now complete.
6. Invite someone to look through the box. The person is able to see objects on the other side of the box, just as if he or she were looking directly at them. The person will assume that he or she is looking directly at the objects. That person will be surprised when you insert a solid object, such as book, into the slot. The person can still see "through" the box.

This project shows a simple but very important principle: things are not always what they seem to be. When performing scientific experiments, the observations made must be carefully considered before reaching any firm conclusions. Never assume the reason for anything you observe. Things that appear to be obvious often turn out to be untrue.

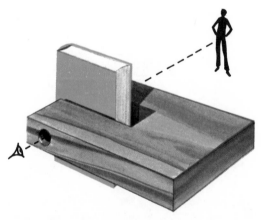

This device makes it seem as if you can look through a solid book, when actually you are looking around it using mirrors.

MOTION PICTURE

Many fascinating devices for demonstrating motion pictures were invented during the 1800s. One such invention was William Horner's *Daedaleum*, which was patented in 1834. Build a version of this simple device and make your own motion pictures.

Materials Needed:
cardboard
cutting knife
glue
strip of paper
pencil

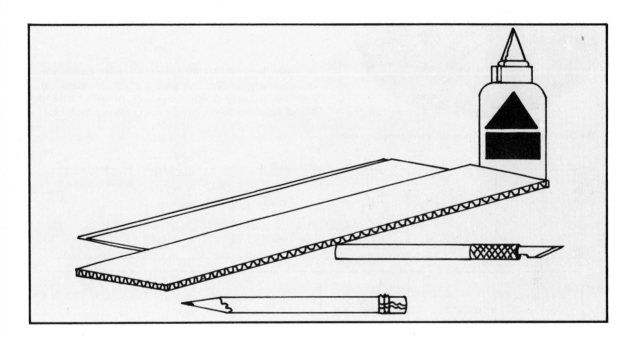

Procedure:

1. Cut out a piece of thin cardboard, size 30 × 10 cm [12 × 4 in].
2. Cut out 12 slots in the cardboard. The slots should be 0.6 cm [0.25 in] in width, 5 cm [2 in] in length, and positioned as shown in the diagram. The distance from one slot to the next should be 2.54 cm [1 in].
3. Make the cardboard into a cylinder by gluing together the short ends. Allow an overlap of 0.5 cm [0.2 in].
4. Trace each series of 12 drawings as shown onto strips of paper 30 cm [12 in] long. Glue the ends of each piece of paper together to form loops. Be sure the illustrations are on the inside. The dotted lines on the diagrams show the amount of overlap to allow when gluing the ends together.
5. Stand the cylinder centrally on the turntable of a record player. The slots should be at the top. Insert one of the paper loops in the bottom of the cylinder. Look through one of the slots so that part of one of the pictures can be seen. Switch on the turntable, preferably at a speed of 78 r.p.m. As the cylinder turns, each picture can be seen in quick succession, giving the impression of a single, moving picture. Now try drawing and demonstrating your own motion pictures.

As the cylinder (left) turns around, each picture will be seen very briefly through the slots. Because the cylinder turns so quickly, the pictures will seem to blend together and become one moving picture.

The *Daedaleum*, a motion-picture device invented in 1834.

PROJECTS FOR VOLUME 14

PALEONTOLOGY

FIELD PROJECT

Huge dinosaurs roamed the earth millions of years ago. We know what these great beasts looked like because fossil remains of their bones and teeth have been found in rocks. Scientists have been able to reconstruct their skeletons by wiring together the pieces. Using fossils to study life from past geological periods is called paleontology.

Dinosaur fossils are rare. But there are millions of smaller fossils in the rocks. To search for these fossils, you need a strong hammer and a steel chisel. A geological map is useful as it shows the kinds of rocks found in the area.

Procedure:

Study the map carefully and avoid looking for fossils in granites and other igneous rocks. These have formed from molten material and contain no fossils. Coarse sandstones are rarely worth looking at either. The best rocks for fossils are clays, shales (hardened and layered clays), and limestones. Some limestones are composed almost entirely of shells and other fossils.

Out in the field, you must find a place where the rocks are exposed. This could be alongside a road or railway cutting, a cliff, or a quarry. Fossils are often harder than the surrounding rock and will have been left standing out from the rock face when the rock was worn away by the weather. Look for such fossils, and look for those that may have fallen to the foot of a cliff. Work systematically at the rock with your hammer and chisel.

Do not simply hack away at random. Many rocks split most readily along certain planes. These are the bedding planes on which the original material was laid down. Fossils are most likely to be found here.

A fossil can be a hollow mold—an impression in the rock showing where the bone or shell once sat—or it can be the cast of an object. Some casts come cleanly away from the rock, leaving a mold, too. But many casts remain firmly embedded. Do not try to get them out. Instead, chip out the piece of rock that contains them. Make it as small as possible so that it is not too heavy to carry home. If a fossil is already cracked when you find it in the rock, take an impression of it with modeling clay. If the fossil breaks up when you try to chip it out, you can still make a plaster cast of the impression you have taken. (*See* CAST-ING PROJECT.)

Wrap your fossils in newspapers to carry them home. Use an old toothbrush for cleaning dirt out of crevices in the fossil shells. An ice pick or similar instrument will be useful for removing harder pieces of rock. When you have cleaned your fossils, try to identify them using books. Or take them to a museum to compare them with other specimens. Label your collection, and note the name of the place where each specimen was found. Also, note the types of rocks in which you found the fossils.

If you find a really large fossil, do not try to remove it from the rock yourself. Instead, tell your local museum about your find. It is best to let experts deal with major discoveries of this kind.

A FOSSIL COLLECTION

horsetail stem

seed fern

scale tree bark

trilobite

ammonite

horsetail leaves

graptolites

PANTOGRAPH

With this pantograph, you can copy drawings at one-half or one-third their original size. It is a useful instrument for making small copies of maps and diagrams.

Construction details are shown in the diagram. Be sure to calculate and mark the locations of the holes accurately. Otherwise, your copies can be distorted.

When the pantograph has been assembled, move the tracer over the drawing or diagram you want to copy. The weighted pencil then traces out a copy. The size of the copy depends upon the way the pantograph is assembled. As shown, it reproduces drawings at half-size. For third-size reproduction, put the pencil into the other thread spool, and bolt the bar AF to holes B and E. Make sure that the joints do not wobble, but be sure they are not too tight.

Materials needed:

3 wood strips 6 × .6 × 40 cm [2.5 × .25 × 16 in]
1 wood strip 6 × .6 × 20 cm [2.5 × .25 × 8 in]
5 nuts and bolts about 6 cm [2.5 in] with washers
piece of 5 cm [2 in] pipe about 6 cm [2.5 in] long
  with a wooden spool glued to one end

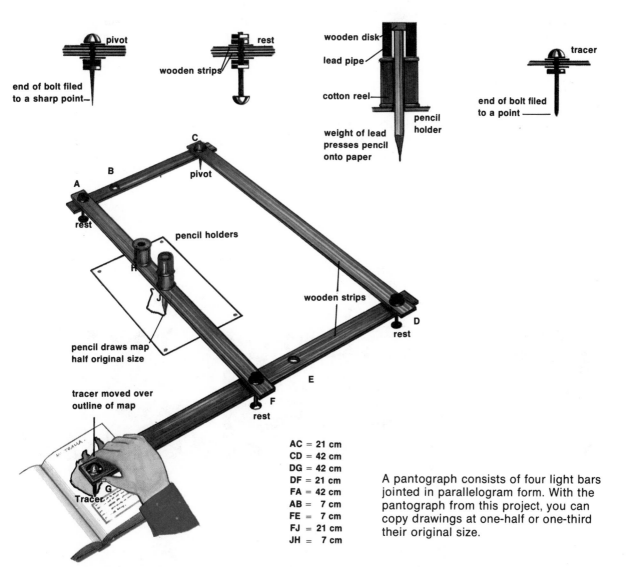

AC = 21 cm
CD = 42 cm
DG = 42 cm
DF = 21 cm
FA = 42 cm
AB = 7 cm
FE = 7 cm
FJ = 21 cm
JH = 7 cm

A pantograph consists of four light bars jointed in parallelogram form. With the pantograph from this project, you can copy drawings at one-half or one-third their original size.

PROJECT FOR VOLUME 15

POLLUTION

Pollution

Fresh, clean water is rich in dissolved oxygen. The more polluted a body of water is, the less dissolved oxygen is present in it. Very polluted water has no dissolved oxygen. Tiny organisms, called pollution indicators, live in water that contains a certain amount of dissolved oxygen.

Procedure:

1. Collect a sample of water from a nearby stream, river, or pond. The organisms present in the sample will indicate how polluted the water is.
2. Look at these organisms with a magnifying glass (MG). Some may only be visible through a microscope at low magnification power (LP) or high magnification power (HP). The arrows in the diagram show whether these organisms live in very polluted or not-so-polluted water.

1. Tubifex worms (MG).
2. *Sphaerotilus* bacteria: top, a colony (LP): bottom, a sheath of bacterial cells (HP).
3. *Eristalis* larva, the "rat-railed maggot" (LP).
4. *Chironomus* larva, "blood worms" on a piece of leaf (MG).
5. *Eudorina*, a green alga (LP). Other algae is often seen.
6. *Vorticella*, a stalked protozoan (LP).
7. *Colpidium,* a very common protozoan (LP).

MEASURING WATER POLLUTION BY OBSERVING ORGANISMS

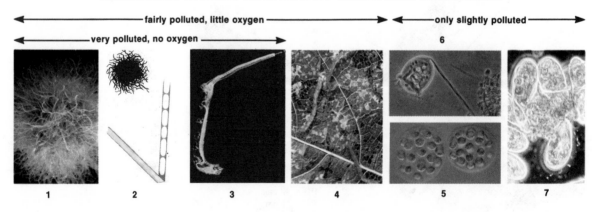

1   2   3   4   5   7

PROJECTS FOR VOLUME 16

PRESSURE

Air pressure can support a column of water or other liquid. For example, take a glass of water with a straw in it. You know that if you suck through the straw, the water will come up through the straw into your mouth. When you suck through the straw, you reduce the air pressure inside the straw. This means that the pressure inside the straw is less than the pressure outside the straw. The air pressure outside the straw is pushing down on the surface of the water in the glass. This pressure forces the water to go up through the straw. In this experiment, you will use air pressure to support a column of liquid.

Procedure:
1. Fill a glass almost to the brim with water.
2. Place a piece of paper over the top of the glass. It is a good idea to use glossy paper or cardboard. Neither will get soggy as quickly as some other types of paper.
3. Holding the paper in place, turn the glass upside down.
4. Remove your hand from the paper. The paper should stay where it is, and the water should stay in the glass.

AIR PRESSURE EXPERIMENT

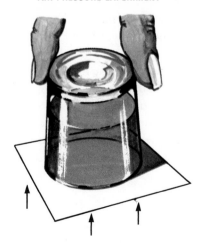

Air pressure supports the paper and water.

Materials Needed:
thick paper or cardboard
flat piece of glass or mirror
water glass
soapy water
table

Experiment 2
In 1654, Otto von Guericke, a German scientist, performed the now famous "Magdeburg Hemispheres" experiment. A hemisphere is similar to a basketball that has been cut in half. In this experiment, von Guericke placed two hemispheres together and pumped out most of the air between them. He used metal hemispheres. Once the air had been pumped out, von Guericke tried to pull the hemispheres apart. He could not separate them. Then he chained each hemisphere to a team of eight horses. These sixteen powerful animals were barely able to pull the hemispheres apart. The hemispheres were held together by the air pressure on their outside surfaces.

Procedure
1. Wet the piece of glass in the soapy water.
2. Place the wet glass on a smooth, horizontal plastic surface.
3. Try to lift the piece of glass up from the table. It will probably seem that the glass is glued to the table. Air cannot reach the underside of the glass because the soapy water fills any small gaps between the glass and the table. Therefore, the air pressure on the underside of the piece of glass is zero. The air pressure on the top of the glass is what keeps it in place.

PRINTING

In letterpress printing, a raised image of a letter or illustration is covered with ink and pressed onto a piece of paper. In this experiment, you will use a potato to print your own designs.

Materials Needed:
raw potato
small knife
paint brush
paint
paper

Procedure:
1. Cut a large potato in half with a knife.
2. Cut away part of the potato to leave a simple shape, such as a triangle or square, standing out.
3. Put some paint on the shape you have cut in the potato. You can either brush on the paint, or dip the shape into a saucer that has a little paint in it.

4. To print the colored shape, press the potato onto a sheet of paper. Build up a pattern by printing the shape several times. You can also use several different shapes and colors to make your design even more interesting.

MAKING POTATO PRINTS

applying paint to a potato printing block

PROPELLER

This propeller-driven balsa-wood car will run well on a smooth floor. When connected to the battery, the electric motor spins the propeller rapidly. Because the propeller blades are twisted, air is forced away from the propeller when it spins. The force exerted on the air is an action, to which there is an equal and opposite reaction. The reaction on the car makes it move in the opposite direction to the airflow.

Procedure:
1. Buy the wheels, motor, and propeller (try a craft or hobby shop) and cut the base and motor support from sheet balsa wood, 1 cm [0.4 in] thick. Choose the size to suit the parts you have bought.
2. Glue the wooden parts together. Glue the propeller onto the motor shaft, and attach the motor and wheels to the car. Keep the battery in place with rubber bands.

3. Place the car on a flat surface and connect the battery to the motor, as shown in the picture. The propeller should spin rapidly, making the car move. By reversing the battery leads, you can change the direction in which the propeller spins. This will reverse the direction in which the car moves.

MAKING A PROPELLER-DRIVEN TROLLEY

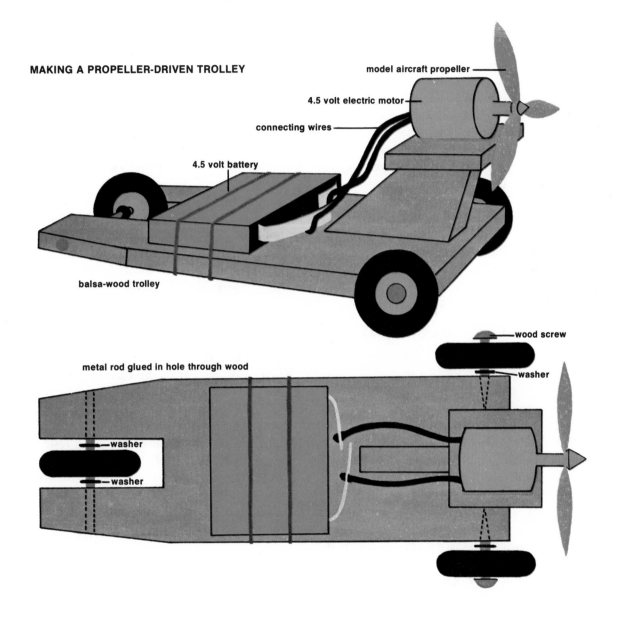

PROJECT FOR VOLUME 17

RESPIRATORY SYSTEM

Every time you breathe, you take in and give off a certain amount of air. The amount exchanged in normal breathing is your tidal capacity. The amount exchanged in heavy breathing is your vital capacity. Some air is always in the lungs. This is called your residual capacity. Your total lung capacity is the greatest amount of air that can be in your lungs at any one time. In this experiment, you will measure your own tidal, vital, and total capacities.

Materials Needed:
2 one-gallon milk bottles made of plastic
about 30 cm [1 ft] of rubber tubing
a measuring cup
a marking pencil that will write on the bottle

Procedure:
1. Put about 0.5 liters [2 cups] of water in the measuring cup. Pour this into the large bottle and mark the level on the bottle. Keep pouring this amount and marking the bottle until it is completely filled with water.
2. Fill a large sink about halfway with water. Carefully turn the bottle upside down so that its neck is under the water. Try not to let any water leak out of the bottle when you turn it over. Put one end of the rubber tube into the neck of the bottle as shown in the illustration. You will breathe into the other end of the tube.
3. To measure tidal capacity, breathe normally a few times, concentrating on each breath. Inhale normally, then exhale normally into the tube. You may want to blow into the tube or to try to fill the bottle with air, but don't do this. Try to exhale a normal breath into the bottle. Measure the amount of air in the bottle by matching its level with the markings you put

on the bottle earlier. This amount should be fairly small—less than 1 liter [1 quart]. This amount is your tidal capacity. Write this number on a piece of paper and mark it "tidal capacity." Fill the bottle with water before going on to the next part.
4. To measure vital capacity, breathe deeply a few times. After inhaling deeply, blow as much air as you can into the tube. Since you will probably be able to fill the bottle completely with air, you should use two bottles. When one bottle is filled with air, quickly move the tube into the second bottle while you are still exhaling. Measure the total amount of air in the bottles. This is your vital capacity. Write this number on the piece of paper and mark it "vital capacity."
5. The residual capacity is the amount of air that stays in the lungs. It is difficult to measure. For this experiment, assume that your residual capacity is about 1.4 liters [1.5 quarts].
6. Your total capacity can be figured from the results of earlier parts of the experiment. Total Capacity = Vital Capacity + Residual Capacity.

It may be interesting to try this experiment with people you know. Compare the capacities of people who smoke and people who don't smoke, and the capacities of athletes and non-athletes.

What can you say about each of these groups? Which group had the largest vital capacities? Why? Which group had the smallest vital capacities? Why?

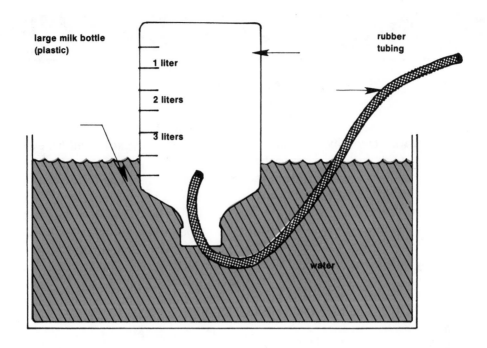

large milk bottle
(plastic)

1 liter

2 liters

3 liters

rubber
tubing

water

PROJECTS FOR VOLUME 18
SENSE

Eyes and Distance

Have you ever wondered why a human being has two eyes and two ears instead of one each? It certainly helps in case one eye or ear is damaged, but it helps more than that. Two eyes or two ears give a person much more information than a single sense organ. For example, two eyes enable a person to judge distances very accurately. This can be proven by performing a simple experiment.

Procedure:

1. Stand a pencil up on end on a table. Cover one eye and then try to put a finger tip quickly onto the point of the pencil. It is very difficult to do this the first time. Further tries are much more likely to succeed because the brain learns by its first mistake and adjusts the arm actions accordingly.

2. Move the pencil to a different position. Try the experiment with both eyes open. It is very easy to touch the point the first time. The explanation is that to focus on the point, the eyes have to swivel inward. The brain, knowing exactly how much the eyes have turned, works out the distance automatically. It then sends the finger to exactly the right point. This swiveling of the eyes does not occur when using only one eye. The head is turned instead.

3. Investigate the swiveling of the eyes by getting a friend to help. Hold your finger about 61 cm [2 ft] in front of the person's nose. Ask him or her to concentrate on the finger tip. Move your finger slowly toward your friend's face. Watch his or her eyes turn inward as they follow the pencil. The closer the object is, the more the eyes have to turn inward.

Ears and Direction

Two ears are better at finding direction than one because a sound to one side affects one ear more than the other. By means of a simple experiment, however, the ears can be confused. A friend's help is needed, along with two coins.

Procedure:

Ask your friend to shut his eyes. Then tap the coins or pebbles together at various points around his head. Vary the loudness of the sounds you make. Ask the person to point out the directions from which these sounds come. The person should guess correctly. But if the coins are tapped directly in front of his head, or directly behind it, both ears are stimulated to the same extent. Your friend will not know whether the the sound is coming from in front, on top, or from behind.

The Sense of Touch

You normally know when anything touches the skin. But not all parts of the body are equally sensitive. This can be shown by investigating the sensitivity of a friend's hands, arms, legs, and back.

Procedure:

Press two pointed sticks lightly onto the person's skin. Ask how many points he or she can feel. (The person should have both eyes closed or be blindfolded.) Sometimes use both points, 1 or 2 cm [0.5 or 1 in] apart, and sometimes use only one point. In this way, the person does not know in advance how many points there are. He or she will always be able to detect the two points on his or her fingers. But when the points are pressed onto the back of the neck, or the middle of the back, the person may only feel one point. These regions are less sensitive to touch. They have fewer nerve endings in the skin. Two points close together may both stimulate the same nerve ending and result in the person feeling only one point. Always be sure to make contact with the two points at the same time.

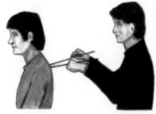

SIPHON

A siphon is a useful device for moving liquid from one container to another at a lower level. In its simplest form, a siphon consists of a bent hose or tube through which the liquid flows. This project tells you how to make a siphon work, and how to use the siphon principle to make a miniature fountain.

The Simple Siphon

1. Place a bucket of water on a table, and an empty bucket on the floor. Place one end of a length of rubber tubing in the top bucket, and suck at the other end until the tube is full of water.

2. Leave one end of the tube in the water, and place your finger over the other end. Put this end of the tube into the empty bucket on the floor. On releasing your finger from the tube, water will start to flow into the lower bucket. It will continue to flow as long as the top end of the tube is under water. This illustrates the basic principle of the siphon. (*See* SIPHON.)

The Siphon Fountain

Siphon action can be demonstrated in a more spectacular way by setting up the apparatus shown in the diagram. If you do not have a flask, you can use any other glass container fitted with a cork or rubber stopper.

Procedure:

1. Drill or cut two holes through the stopper and insert into them two pieces of glass tubing. The end of the longer piece of tubing in the flask should be tapered.

2. Arrange the apparatus as shown in the diagram, using food coloring to color the water.

3. Suck the lower tube until water starts to flow

down it. Then quickly remove your mouth from the tube to avoid sucking up the colored water into your mouth.

4. Place the lower tube in the bucket on the floor. As before, water will pass from the upper bucket to the lower one. But, in this case, the water will pass through the flask first, forming a fountain.

MAKING A SIPHON FOUNTAIN

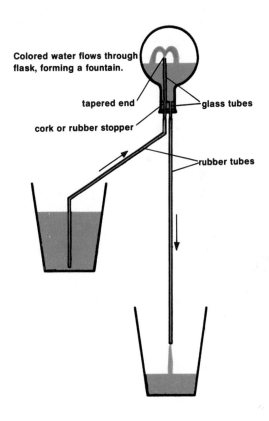

Colored water flows through flask, forming a fountain.

tapered end

glass tubes

cork or rubber stopper

rubber tubes

SNAIL

FIELD PROJECT

Have you ever walked around a garden or along a country road after a summer shower and seen the many snails that come out to enjoy the moist conditions? It would be almost impossible to count all the snails. However, there is a simple method for making an accurate estimate of the numbers in a given area.

Procedure:

Select a distinct area of your garden, or a distinct stretch of roadside area, and collect snails from all parts of the area. The more you get, the more accurate your results will be. It will make the calculations easier if you collect a round number, such as 20 or 50. Mark each snail you collect with a small dot of paint. Do not use extremely bright colors as these might attract birds and upset the results. Blue, green, or brown are good as long as you can easily see the spots when you examine the snails later.

After marking the snails, release them evenly over the area from which they were collected. Leave them for a day or two to mingle with the rest of the snails in the population. This is very important. The next stage is to catch a second sample from the same area. This must be done at the same time of day and under the same weather conditions as the first sample. Capture as many as you can. You should find that some of the snails in the new sample bear the paint marks you made. Count the numbers of marked and unmarked snails in this new sample.

As long as the snails were allowed to mingle freely when the marked ones were released, the second sample can be taken as representative of the population as a whole. The proportion of marked snails in the second sample will thus be about the same as the proportion of marked snails in the whole population.

ESTIMATING A SNAIL POPULATION

marking a snail

Calculating the Population

Suppose 50 snails were marked. The proportion of marked snails in the whole population is then $\frac{50}{P}$, where P represents the total population. Suppose that 20 snails were then caught in the second sample and that, of these, 5 bore marks. The proportion of marked snails in this case would be $\frac{5}{20}$. This would also be the proportion of marked snails in the total population. So we can say that $\frac{5}{20} = \frac{50}{P}$. Therefore, $P = \frac{50 \times 20}{5}$, which = 200 snails. In general, P is equal to $\frac{A \times B}{C}$, where A is the number originally marked, B is the total number of snails in the second sample, and C is the number of marked snails in sample B.

This method gives an estimate of the entire population in the area studied. It can be used for various kinds of animals, but only for those animals that do not move about too much. It is usually of no use for animals such as butterflies, which can move in and out of an area very easily. The method has, however, been used to estimate butterfly populations on small islands, where few insects leave and few new ones arrive.

Eight snails (blue box) are marked with paint spots. They are then released and allowed to mingle freely with all the other snails in the population (black box). Later, a typical sample of 15 snails (red box) is found to contain two marked snails. So the total of eight marked snails must be distributed in a total population of about (8 ÷ 2) × 15 = 60 snails.

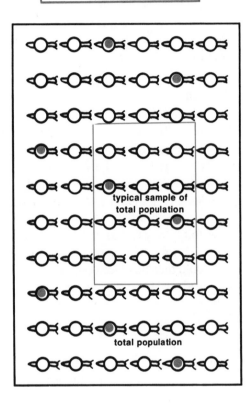

marked sample

typical sample of total population

total population

PROJECT FOR VOLUME 19

SURFACE TENSION

A steel needle can float on water. A model boat can be propelled by soap. These things are possible because liquids behave as if a skin coats their surface. This effect is called surface tension. Show surface tension by doing the experiments described below.

Materials Needed:

water glass	paper clip
steel needle	piece of wire
tissue paper	piece of thread
piece of soap	container, such as dishpan
half a matchbox	

Experiment 1
Procedure:

1. Fill a glass with water. Hold a small steel needle horizontally, just above the surface of the water. The needle should be as close to the water as possible. If the needle is cautiously released, it should rest on the surface of the water, held there by surface tension.

2. Another way to float the needle is to put it on a small scrap of absorbent tissue paper, which should then be placed on the water. The paper absorbs water and sinks, leaving the needle on the surface.

Experiment 2
Procedure:

1. Use the bottom of a matchbox as a model boat. Attach a small piece of soap to the back of the boat with the paper clip. Make sure the soap does not touch the sides or front of the boat.

2. Fill a clean container with clean water. Place the matchbox boat in the water. The soap should start to dissolve, lowering the surface tension at the back of the boat. The greater surface tension in front of the boat pulls it through the water. When all the water becomes soapy, the boat will no longer move.

Experiment 3
Procedure:

1. Make a round wire loop, about 4 cm [1.5 in] wide, with a twisted wire handle. (See picture.)

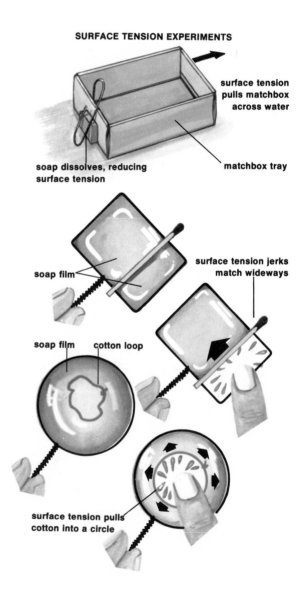

SURFACE TENSION EXPERIMENTS

surface tension pulls matchbox across water

soap dissolves, reducing surface tension

matchbox tray

soap film

surface tension jerks match wideways

soap film   cotton loop

surface tension pulls cotton into a circle

2. Tie a piece of thread, about 8 cm [3 in] long, into a loop.

3. Dip the wire loop into soapy water. A soap film should form over the loop.

4. Carefully place the loop of thread onto the soap film. It should have a "loose," wobbly shape. Now burst the film inside the thread loop. Surface tension will pull the piece of thread into a circle.

PROJECTS FOR VOLUME 20

TELESCOPE

With simple materials you can make two kinds of telescopes.

Materials Needed:
2 cardboard tubes, one a little wider than the other
3 converging (curving out) lenses
1 diverging (curving in) lens
glue

Making an Astronomical Telescope
Procedure:
1. The objective lens (the one nearer the object being observed) should have a relatively large diameter and long focal length. A diameter of 5 cm [2 in] works well. A suitable focal length is about 50 cm [20 in]. Check the focal length by focusing an image of the sun onto a white card. When the sun is focused, the distance between the lens and card is equal to the focal length of the lens. The eyepiece lens can be smaller in diameter. It should have a focal length of about 5 cm [2 in].

2. Build the telescope with the two cardboard tubes. The length of the wider tube should be about equal to the focal length of the objective lens. Make the narrower tube a little shorter. Slide the narrower tube a little way into the wider tube.

3. Glue the two lenses in position, making sure they are not crooked. To prevent the tubes coming apart, glue thin rings of cardboard inside them, as shown in the diagram.

4. When the glue is dry, point the telescope at a distant object. Focus by sliding the small tube in or out of the large one. You should be able to form a sharp, enlarged, inverted image of the object.

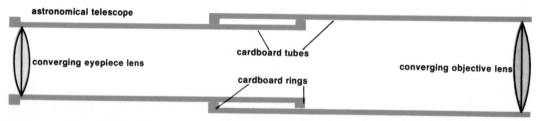

astronomical telescope
converging eyepiece lens
cardboard tubes
cardboard rings
converging objective lens

Making a Galilean Telescope
The Galilean telescope is made in the same way as the astronomical telescope. The only difference is that the eyepiece lens is concave instead of convex. This means that it is diverging instead of converging. The telescope forms an upright image.

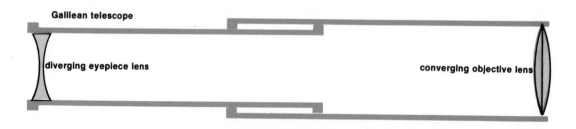

Galilean telescope
diverging eyepiece lens
converging objective lens

TORTOISE

Keeping a pet tortoise

When buying a tortoise, such as a box turtle, there are three things you should look for. As soon as you pick it up, it should draw its legs and head into its shell. If it does not react in this way, it may be unhealthy. If you are looking at two tortoises that seem the same size, choose the one which is heavier. It has eaten more during infancy and is therefore likely to be healthier and live longer. Also, a tortoise's eyes should be bright and not watering.

The sex of a tortoise can be known by looking at the underpart of its shell. In males, this is curved toward the rear end. Also, the tail is longer and stouter than that of the female. In females, the underside of the shell is flat and the tail is shorter.

Materials Needed:
one healthy tortoise
wooden box
wire netting (such as chicken wire)
shallow water dish
straw
regular supply of green plants

Procedure:
1. Tortoises are best kept outside in a yard or garden. It is a good idea to keep them inside a wire-netting fence. They can easily get lost if allowed to roam freely. Keep your fence about 50 cm [20 in] high. It should be dug well into the ground so the tortoise cannot dig under it.
2. For nighttime shelter, use a covered wooden box. Line it with straw, and change the straw often.
3. Give the tortoise drinking water in a large shallow dish. The water can also be used as a pool for the tortoise in warm weather.
4. Feed your tortoise fresh green plants. Tortoises like most green plants, including garden plants. (This is another reason for not giving tortoises a free run.) Tortoises should be fed daily. Their appetite varies widely.

adult tortoise

5. In cold weather, small tortoises should be kept indoors in a warm room. Larger tortoises may hibernate in winter. They should be put in a large cardboard box, well filled with dried leaves, hay, or crumpled newspaper. Make sure there are air holes in the top, and do not fasten it down. Once tortoises have gone to sleep, they should not be disturbed. Tortoises awake from hibernation when the warm spring weather comes.

Sometimes tortoises manage to turn themselves onto their backs. Usually they can right themselves, but this should not be left to chance. After more than a few hours in this position, the weight of their body organs pressing the wrong way can kill them.

Tortoises have small brains. They cannot be described as being intelligent animals, but they can recognize their owners, probably through their keen sense of smell. Tortoises seem to be short-sighted, but they can distinguish colors, especially yellows and reds.

KEEPING TORTOISES

Above, an outdoor pen for keeping tortoises. It is important to have a fence to keep them from escaping, a straw-filled box for shelter, and a large water dish.

PROJECTS FOR VOLUME 21

VAPOR

In the atmosphere, clouds form when air containing water vapor cools. The cooler air cannot hold so much water vapor, so some of the vapor condenses to form clouds. This project shows how to simulate this effect—how to form a cloud in a glass jar.

MAKING A CLOUD

balloon rubber

string

water vapor

water

water vapor condenses to form a cloud when rubber is released

cloud

Materials Needed:
large glass jar
chalk powder
thin rubber sheet (cut from balloon)
string

Procedure:
1. Pour a little water into a glass jar. Cover the jar with its lid, or with a book, and leave it for about 15 minutes.
2. Uncover the jar and put some chalk powder inside. Immediately cover the jar with a thin rubber sheet cut from a large balloon.
3. Compress the air in the jar by pressing the rubber in with your fist. The air becomes warmer and absorbs more water vapor. After 15 seconds, release the rubber. The air cools. Some of the water vapor condenses on the chalk dust, forming a cloud.

WORM

Earthworms are some of the most important animals in the soil of gardens and farms. They tunnel through the soil, bringing air to the roots and forming passageways for water to drain from the surface. As they tunnel, they "eat" soil and bring it from one level to another. Many of the activities of earthworms can be watched and studied by setting up a simple wormery.

Materials Needed:
two pieces of glass or clear plastic, about 25 cm [10 in] square.
piece of wood 3 cm [1.2 in] thick
glue
different kinds of soil
strainer made of wire screen
piece of black plastic or plastic-coated cardboard
earthworms

Procedure:
1. Form the wood into a three-sided frame along the glass squares, as shown in the picture. Two short pieces of wood can be glued to the bottom of the frame to help it stand up more easily.
2. Glue the glass or plastic to each side of the frame to make a rectangular container as shown.
3. Fill the container with soil. Run the soil through the strainer to remove any large stones. Pour the soil into the wormery in layers, each about 3 cm [1.2 in] thick. You might even put a layer of gravel halfway up. As you put in each layer, sprinkle it with water. Do not add so much water that it forms a pool, though.

4. Add earthworms. You can get these from your garden or lawn. The best time to collect them is at night. You can also buy earthworms from a store that sells bait to fishermen. Put the worms in the wormery and watch them start to burrow. Add some dead leaves and grass clippings to the surface. Sprinkle some water on these leaves or clippings. Cover the top of the wormery with a piece of black plastic, or plastic-coated cardboard. Do not leave the wormery in the sunlight.

Observing the wormery
Examine your wormery every day. You will soon see that the soil layers are being mixed up as the worms tunnel through them. Soil from the upper layers falls into the lower layers as the tunnels collapse. But how does soil get from the lower layers to the upper layers? If you put in a layer of gravel, you should be able to see it sink slowly toward the bottom of the wormery. You may even be able to measure the rate at which it sinks. The gravel particles are too large for a worm to swallow, so the gravel layer sinks as the worms remove the soil from beneath this layer.

You will also be able to see how the worms move in their tunnels by anchoring one part of the body and then pushing or pulling the rest of the body forward. How does the worm anchor itself? How can you tell which end of the worm is the head? Every few days, check to be sure that the soil is moist and that there is plenty of food—dead leaves—on the surface.

MAKING A WORMERY

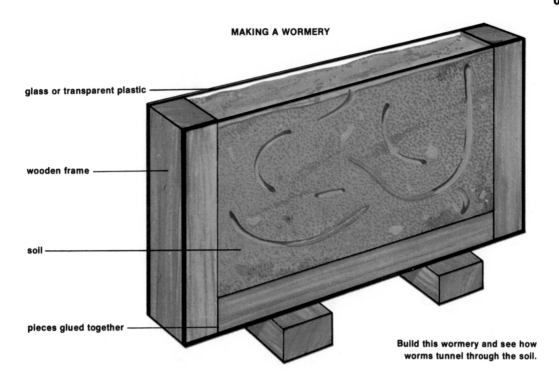

glass or transparent plastic

wooden frame

soil

pieces glued together

Build this wormery and see how worms tunnel through the soil.

YEAST

A yeast is a fungus. It is a living organism that feeds on sugar and gives off carbon dioxide (a gas) and either alcohol or water. Yeasts are used in making bread, beer, and many other carbonated drinks. In this experiment, you will grow some yeasts. You can buy yeasts at any grocery store or supermarket. You might even have some at home. Yeast is sold in both powdered and cake form. Either one will work in this experiment.

Materials Needed:
8 soda pop bottles
8 balloons
yeasts
water
sugar solution (can be made by mixing equal parts of water and sugar or honey)

Procedure:
1. Fill four of the bottles about halfway with the sugar solution. Mark these bottles with an "S."

2. Fill the other four bottles about halfway with plain water. Mark these four bottles with a "W." Be sure that the sugar solutions and water are at about room temperature, 18 to 26°C [65 to 80°F].

3. Add a teaspoonful of yeast to two of the bottles with the sugar solution. Mark these two bottles with a "Y." You should now have two bottles that are marked with both "S" and "Y."

4. Add a teaspoonful of yeast to two of the bottles with plain water. Mark these two bottles with a "Y." You should now have two bottles that are marked with both "W" and "Y."

5. Put a balloon on the top of each of the eight bottles. Divide the bottles into two groups. Each group should have a plain water bottle ("W"), a water and yeast bottle ("W" and "Y"), a sugar solution bottle ("S"), and a sugar solution with yeast bottle ("S" and "Y").

6. Place one of these groups of four bottles in the refrigerator. Place the other group in a warm

place, such as near—but not touching—a radiator.

Check all the bottles every few hours. What happens to the liquid in each of the eight bottles? What happens to the balloons on each of the eight bottles? Is there a difference between the yeasts in the plain water and those in the sugar solutions? Is there a difference between the yeast growth in the bottles kept in the refrigerator and those kept in a warm place? In which bottles did nothing at all happen? Why is this? What conclusions can you make about what yeast needs in order to grow?

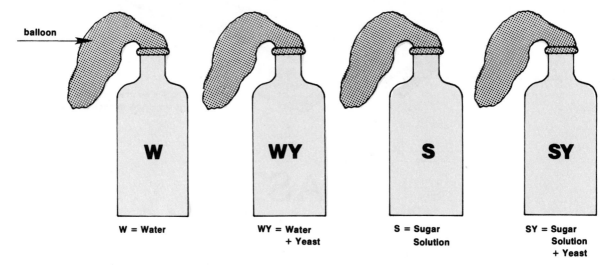

Put four bottles, each with a different liquid, in the refrigerator for several hours. Compare what happens to each balloon and each liquid.

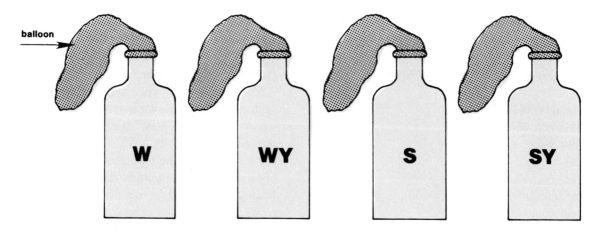

Put the other four bottles in a warm place for several hours. Notice what happens to each balloon and each liquid. Compare what happens in each of the eight bottles.

BIBLIOGRAPHY

AGRICULTURE AND ANIMAL HUSBANDRY

Brown, Lester R. *Increasing World Food Output*. Arno, 1976. YA

Carne, Barbara, and Mills, Bruce. *A Basic Guide to Horse Care and Management*. Arco, 1979. YA

Charles, Elizabeth. *How to Keep Your Pet Healthy*. Macmillan, 1974. J

Cobb, Nathan, and Cole, John. *Cityside—Countryside*. Stephen Greene, 1980. YA

Cole, H. H., and Ronning, Magnar. *Animal Agriculture*. 2nd ed. Freeman, 1980. YA

Ebeling, Walter. *The Fruited Plain*. University of California Press, 1981. YA

Encyclopedia of American Agricultural History. Greenwood, 1975. YA

Jacobs, Herbert. *A Practical Guide for the Beginning Farmer*. Dover, 1978. YA

Johl, S. S., ed. *Irrigation and Agricultural Development*. Pergamon, 1980. YA

Lee, Hollis. *Country Home and Small Farm Handbook*. Van Nostrand Reinhold, 1983. YA

Leinwohl, Stanley. *The Book of Pets*. Messner, 1980. YA

Monich, Jerry, and Hunt, Marjorie. *The Rodale Guide to Composting*. Rodale, 1979. YA

Nearing, Helen, and Scott. *Continuing the Good Life: Half a Century of Homesteading*. Schocken, 1980. YA

Weisbud, Claudia. *Raising Your Own Livestock*. Prentice-Hall, 1980. YA

West, Geoffrey P. *Encyclopedia of Animal Care*. 12th ed. Williams & Wilkinson, 1977. YA

AMPHIBIANS AND REPTILES

Behler, John L., and King, F. W. *The Audubon Society Field Guide to North American Reptiles and Amphibians*. Knopf, 1979. YA

Billings, Charlene W. *Salamanders*. Dodd, Mead, 1981. J

Cloudsley-Thompson, J. L. *Crocodiles and Alligators*. McGraw-Hill, 1977. J

Cochran, Doris M., and Goin, Coleman J. *The New Field Book of Reptiles and Amphibians*. Putnam, 1978. YA

Cole, Joanna. *A Frog's Body*. Morrow, 1980. J

Cole, Joanna. *A Snake's Body*. Morrow, 1981. J

DeGraaf, Richard M. *Amphibians and Reptiles of New England*. University of Massachusetts Press, 1983. YA

Fichter, George S. *Poisonous Snakes*. Watts, 1982. J

Freedman, Russell. *Killer Snakes*. Holiday, 1982. J

Graham, Ada, and Frank. *Alligators*. Delacorte, 1979. YA

Gross, Ruth Belov. *Alligators and Other Crocodilians*. Four Winds, 1978. J

Harris, Susan. *Reptiles*. Watts, 1978. J

Leen, Nina. *Snakes*. Holt, Rinehart & Winston, 1978. J

Ommanney, Francis Downes. *Frogs, Toads, and Newts*. McGraw-Hill, 1975. J

Patent, Dorothy H. *Reptiles and How They Reproduce*. Holiday, 1977. J

Pinney, Roy. *The Snake Book*. Doubleday, 1981. YA

Roever, Joan M. *Snake Secrets*. Walker, 1979. YA

Selsam, Millicent E., and Hunt, Joyce. *A First Look at Frogs, Toads, and Salamanders*. Walker, 1976. J

Simon, Hilda. *Easy Identification Guide to North American Snakes*. Dodd, Mead, 1979. YA

Smith, Hobart M. *Amphibians of North America: A Guide to Field Identification*. Western/Golden, 1978. YA

Zappler, George, and Lisbeth. *Amphibians as Pets*. Doubleday, 1973. J

ASTRONOMY AND SOLAR SYSTEM

Asimov, Isaac. *How Did We Find Out About Outer Space?* Walker, 1977. YA

Asimov, Isaac. *The Universe: From Flat Earth to Black Holes and Beyond*. rev. Walker, 1980. YA

Beatty, J. Kelley, et al., eds. *The New Solar System*. Cambridge University Press, 1981. YA

Bedeler, Werner. *The Fascinating Universe*. Van Nostrand Reinhold, 1983. YA

Berger, Melvin. *Bright Stars, Red Giants and White Dwarfs*. Putnam, 1983. J

Bok, Bart J., and Priscilla F. *The Milky Way*. 5th ed. Harvard University Press, 1981. YA

Brandt, John C., and Chapman, Robert D. *Introduction to Comets*. Cambridge University Press. YA

Branley, Franklyn M. *Halley: Comet 1986*. Dutton/Lodestar, 1983. J

Branley, Franklyn M. *The Planets in Our Solar System*. Harper & Row/Crowell, 1981. J

Branley, Franklyn M. *The Sky Is Full of Stars*. Harper & Row, 1981. J

Branley, Franklyn M. *Sun Dogs and Shooting Stars: A Skywatcher's Calendar*. Houghton Mifflin, 1980. J

Calder, Nigel. *The Comet Is Coming*. Penguin, 1982. YA

Calder, Nigel. *Timescale*. Viking, 1983. YA

Chapman, Clark R. *Planets of Rock and Ice: From Mercury to the Moons of Saturn*. Scribner, 1982. YA

Cooper, Henry S. F. *Imaging Saturn*. Holt, Rinehart & Winston, 1983. YA

Couper, Heather, and Henbest, Nigel. *Astronomy*. Watts, 1983. J

Gallant, Roy A. *National Geographic Picture Atlas of Our Universe*. National Geographic Society, 1980. YA

Gallant, Roy A. *Once Around the Galaxy*. Watts, 1983. YA

Gallant, Roy A. *The Planets: Exploring the Solar System*. Scholastic/Four Winds, 1982. YA

Gibbons, Gail. *Sun Up, Sun Down*. Harcourt Brace Jovanovich, 1983. J

Harrison, Edward R. *Cosmology: The Science of the Universe*. Cambridge University Press, 1981. YA

Jaber, William. *Exploring the Sun*. Messner, 1980. J

Maffei, Paolo. *Monsters in the Sky*. MIT Press, 1980. YA

Mitton, Simon, ed. *The Cambridge Encyclopedia of Astronomy*. Crown, 1977. YA

Moore, Patrick. *Pocket Guide to Astronomy*. Simon & Schuster, 1980. YA

Ronan, Colin. *The Practical Astronomer*. Macmillan, 1981. YA

Sagan, Carl. *Cosmos*. Random House, 1980. YA

Sidgwick, J. B. *Amateur Astronomer's Handbook*. Enslow, 1981. YA

Simon, Seymour. *Earth, Our Planet in Space*. Macmillan/Four Winds, 1984. J

Tombaugh, Clyde, and Moore, Patrick. *Out of the Darkness: The Planet Pluto*. Scribner, 1982. YA

Vogt, Gregory. *Mars and the Inner Planets*. Watts, 1982. J

Washburn, Mark. *In the Light of the Sun*. Harcourt Brace Jovanovich, 1981. YA

ATOM AND RADIOACTIVITY

Asimov, Isaac. *How Did We Find Out About Atoms?* Walker, 1976. J

Asimov, Isaac. *How Did We Find Out About Nuclear Power?* Walker, 1976. J

Asimov, Isaac. *Inside the Atom*. rev. Abelard, 1974. YA

Gallant, Roy A. *Explorers of the Atom*. Doubleday, 1974. J

Lampton, Christopher. *Fusion: The Eternal Flame*. Watts, 1982. YA

Trefil, James S. *From Atoms to Quarks: An Introduction to the Strange World of Particle Physics*. Scribner, 1980. YA

AUTOMATION

Chester, Michael. *Robots: Facts Behind the Fiction*. Macmillan/Collier, 1983. J

Cummings, Richard. *Make Your Own Robots*. McKay, 1981. YA

Lambert, Mark. *50 Facts About Robots*. Warwick; dist. by Watts, 1983. J

Metos, Thomas H. *Robots A–Z*. Messner, 1980. J

Silverstein, Alvin, and Virginia. *The Robots Are Here*. Prentice-Hall, 1983. J

BIOLOGY

Abercrombie, Michael, et al. *Penguin Dictionary of Biology*. Viking, 1977. YA

Anderson, Lucia. *The Smallest Life Around Us*. Crown, 1978. J

Asimov, Isaac. *How Did We Find Out About the Beginning of Life?* Walker, 1982. J

Asimov, Isaac. *How Did We Find Out About Our Human Roots?* Walker, 1979. J

Asimov, Isaac. *A Short History of Biology.* Greenwood, 1980. YA

Bornstein, Jerry, and Sandy. *What Is Genetics?* Messner, 1979. YA

Cherfas, Jeremy. *Man-Made Life.* Pantheon, 1982. YA

Cobb, Vicki. *Lots of Rot.* Lippincott; dist. by Harper & Row, 1981. J

Dixon, Bernard. *Magnificent Microbes.* Atheneum, 1976. YA

Facklam, Margery, and Howard. *From Cell to Clone: The Story of Genetic Engineering.* Harcourt Brace Jovanovich, 1979. J

Hoyle, Fred. *The Intelligent Universe.* Holt, Rinehart & Winston, 1984. YA

Lampton, Christopher. *DNA and the Creation of New Life.* Arco, 1983. YA

McLaughlin, John C. *The Tree of Animal Life: A Tale of Changing Forms and Fortunes.* Dodd, Mead, 1981. J

Marshall, Kim. *The Story of Life: From the Big Bang to You.* Holt, Rinehart & Winston, 1981. YA

Mason, William H. *The Human Side of Biology.* Harper & Row, 1983. YA

Patent, Dorothy H. *Bacteria: How They Affect Other Living Things.* Holiday, 1980. J

Patent, Dorothy H. *Evolution Goes on Every Day.* Holiday, 1977. YA

Stanley, Steven M. *The New Evolutionary Timetable.* Basic Books, 1981. YA

Taylor, Ron. *The Story of Evolution.* Watts/Warwick, 1981. YA

BIRDS

Audubon, John James. *Audubon's Birds of America.* Abrams, 1979. YA

Blassingame, Wyatt. *Wonders of Crows.* Dodd, Mead, 1979. J

Blassingame, Wyatt. *Wonders of Egrets, Bitterns, and Herons.* Dodd, Mead, 1982. J

Bonners, Susan. *Penguin Year.* Delacorte, 1981. J

Bowers, Mary Beacom, ed. *Stories About Birds and Bird Watchers.* Atheneum, 1981. YA

Britton, Dorothy. *The Japanese Crane: Bird of Happiness.* Kodansha, 1981. YA

Cole, Joanna. *A Bird's Body.* Morrow, 1982. J

Freedman, Russell. *How Birds Fly.* Holiday, 1977. J

Friedman, Judi. *Puffins, Come Back!* Dodd, Mead, 1981. J

Gould, John. *John Gould's Birds.* A & W, 1981. J

Harris, Lorie K. *Biography of a Whooping Crane.* Putnam, 1977. J

Harrison, Peter. *Seabirds: An Identification Guide.* Houghton Mifflin, 1983. YA

Hendrich, Paula. *Saving America's Birds.* Lothrop, 1982. J

Hopf, Alice L. *Chickens and Their Wild Relatives.* Dodd, Mead, 1982. J

Isenbart, Hans-Heinrich. *A Duckling Is Born.* Putnam, 1981. J

Karmali, John. *Birds of Africa.* Viking, 1980. YA

Lavine, Sigmund A. *Wonders of Flightless Birds.* Dodd, Mead, 1982. J

McGowen, Ted. *Album of Birds.* Rand McNally, 1982. J

Mead, Chris. *Bird Migration.* Facts on File, 1983. YA

Peterson, Roger Tory. *Field Guides to the Birds.* Houghton Mifflin. (Series.) YA

Selsam, Millicent E. *A First Look at Bird Nests.* Walker, 1985. J

Stonehous, Bernard. *Penguins.* McGraw-Hill, 1980. J

Storms, Laura. *The Bird Book.* Lerner, 1982. J

BOTANY

Bubel, Nancy. *The Seed-Starter's Handbook.* Rodale, 1978. YA

Busch, Phyllis. *Cactus in the Desert.* Harper & Row/Crowell, 1979. J

Elias, Thomas S. *The Complete Trees of North America.* Van Nostrand Reinhold, 1980. YA

Facts on File Dictionary of Botany. Facts on File, 1984. YA

Grimm, William C. *The Illustrated Book of Trees.* Stackpole, 1983. YA

Johnson, Sylvia A. *Mosses.* Lerner, 1983. J

Kavaler, Lucy. *Green Magic: Algae Rediscovered.* Harper & Row/Crowell, 1983. J

Lauber, Patricia. *Seeds: Pop, Stick, Glide.* Crown, 1981. J

Lincoff, Gary H. *The Audubon Society Field Guide to North American Mushrooms.* Knopf, 1981. YA

Pohl, Richard W. *How to Know the Grasses.* 3rd ed. W. C. Brown, 1978. YA

Pringle, Laurence. *Being a Plant.* Harper & Row/Crowell, 1983. J

Riciutti, Edward R. *Plants in Danger.* Harper & Row, 1979. J

Selsam, Millicent E. *A First Look at Flowers.* Walker, 1977. J

Selsam, Millicent E. *Eat the Fruit, Plant the Seed.* Morrow, 1980. J

Selsam, Millicent E. *The Plants We Eat.* rev. Morrow, 1981. J

Stone, Doris M. *The Lives of Plants.* Scribner, 1983. YA

BUILDING CONSTRUCTION

Brooks, Hugh. *Illustrated Encyclopedic Dictionary of Building and Construction Terms.* Prentice-Hall, 1976. YA

Dagostino, Frank R. *Materials of Construction.* Reston, 1982. YA

DeCristoforo, R. J. *DeCristoforo's Housebuilding Illustrated.* Harper & Row, 1978. YA

Feirier, John L. *Carpentry and Building Construction.* Bennett, 1981. YA

Huntington, Whitney Clark, and Mickadeit, Robert E. *Building Construction.* 5th ed. Wiley, 1981. YA

Huth, Mark. *Introduction to Construction.* Delmar, 1980. YA

Salvadori, Mario. *Structure in Architecture.* Prentice-Hall, 1975. YA

CHEMISTRY

Asimov, Isaac. *Asimov on Chemistry.* Doubleday, 1974. YA

Asimov, Isaac. *A Short History of Chemistry: An Introduction to the Ideas and Concepts of Chemistry.* Greenwood, 1978. YA

Brady, James E., and Humiston, Gerard E. *General Chemistry: Principles and Structure.* 2nd ed. Wiley, 1980. YA

Chemistry Education Association. *Chemistry: Key to the Earth.* Melbourne, 1979. YA

Cherrier, Francois. *Fascinating Experiments in Chemistry.* Sterling, 1978. YA

Sisler, Harry H., et al. *Chemistry: A Systematic Approach.* Oxford University Press, 1980. YA

COMMUNICATIONS

Busch, H. Ted, and Landeck, Terry. *The Making of a Television Commercial.* Macmillan, 1980. YA

Consumer Guide Editors. *The Basic Book of Ham Radio.* Simon & Schuster, 1979. YA

Desmond, Robert W. *The Information Process: World News Reporting to the Twentieth Century.* University of Iowa Press, 1979. YA

Grosswirth, Marvin. *Beginner's Guide to Home Video.* Doubleday, 1980. YA

Hasling, John. *Fundamentals of Radio Broadcasting.* McGraw-Hill, 1980. YA

Maltia, Leonard, and Greenfield, Allan. *The Complete Guide to Home Video.* Crown, 1981. YA

Smith, Anthony. *Goodbye Gutenberg: The Newspaper Revolution of the 1980s.* Oxford University Press, 1980. YA

COMPUTERS

Ardley, Neil. *Computers.* Warwick; dist. by Watts, 1983. J

Ault, Rox. *BASIC Programming for Kids.* Houghton Mifflin, 1983. J

Bear, John. *Computer Wimp.* Ten Speed Press, 1983. YA

Berger, Melvin. *Computers in Your Life.* Harper & Row/Crowell, 1981. J

Berger, Melvin. *Data Processing.* Watts, 1983. J

Bertoni, Phil. *Strangers in Computerland.* Lewis, 1983. YA

Bitter, Gary G. *Computers in Today's World.* Wiley, 1984. YA

Christie, Linda G. *The ABCs of Microcomputers.* Prentice-Hall, 1983. YA

Cohen, Daniel, and Susan. *The Kid's Guide to Home Computers.* Pocket/Archway, 1983. J

D'Ignazio, Fred. *Messner's Introduction to the Computer.* Messner, 1983. YA

D'Ignazio, Fred. *Small Computers: Exploring Their Technological Future.* Watts, 1981. YA

Galanter, Eugene. *Kids and Computers.* Perigee, 1983. YA

Graham, Ian. *Computer.* Gloucester; dist. by Watts, 1983. J

Hellman, Hal. *Computer Basics.* Prentice-Hall, 1983. J

Herbert, Frank, and Barnard, Max. *Without Me You're Nothing.* Simon & Schuster, 1981. YA

Hintz, Sandy, and Martin. *Computers in Our World.* Watts, 1983. J

Hyde, Margaret O. *Computers That Think? The Search for Artificial Intelligence.* Enslow, 1982. YA

Richard, Ian. *Computers.* Watts, 1983. J

Spencer, Donald D. *Computer Dictionary for Everyone.* Scribner, 1980. YA

Trombetta, Michael. *BASIC for Students: With Applications.* Addison-Wesley, 1981. YA

Wexelblat, Richard L., ed. *History of Programming Languages.* Academic Press, 1981. YA

EARTH SCIENCE

Aylesworth, Thomas G., and Virginia L. *The Mount St. Helens Disaster: What We've Learned*. Watts, 1983. J

Ballard, Robert D. *Exploring Our Living Planet*. National Geographic Society, 1983. YA

Coburn, Doris K. *A Spit Is a Piece of Land*. Messner, 1982. J

Fodor, R. V. *Chiseling the Earth: How Erosion Shapes the Land*. Enslow, 1983. J

Fodor, R. V. *Earth Afire! Volcanoes and Their Activity*. Morrow, 1981. J

Fodor, R. V. *Frozen Earth: Explaining the Ice Ages*. Enslow, 1981. J

Graham, Ada, and Frank. *The Changing Desert*. Sierra Club; dist. by Scribner, 1981. J

Hurlburt, Cornelius S., Jr., ed. *The Planet We Live On: An Illustrated Encyclopedia of the Earth Sciences*. Abrams, 1976. YA

Kiefer, Irene. *Global Jigsaw Puzzle: The Story of Continental Drift*. Atheneum, 1978. J

Lapedes, Daniel N., et al., eds. *McGraw-Hill Encyclopedia of the Geological Sciences*. McGraw-Hill, 1978. YA

Laycock, George. *Caves*. Four Winds, 1976. J

Miklowitz, Gloria D. *Earthquake!* Messner, 1977. J

Nixon, Hershell H., and Joan Lowery. *Earthquake: Nature in Motion*. Dodd, Mead, 1981. J

Our Violent Earth. National Geographic Society, 1982. J

Simon, Seymour. *Danger from Below: Earthquakes: Past, Present, and Future*. Scholastic/Four Winds, 1979. J

ECOLOGY AND ENVIRONMENT

Bender, David L., and Leone, Bruno, eds. *The Ecology Controversy*. 3rd ed. Greenhaven, 1981. YA

Black, Hallie. *Dirt Cheap: The Evolution of Renewable Resource Management*. Morrow Junior Books, 1979. J

Carson, Rachel. *Silent Spring*. Houghton Mifflin, 1962; Fawcett, 1978. YA

Jaspersohn, William. *How the Forest Grew*. Greenwillow, 1979. J

Lerner, Carol. *On the Forest Edge*. Morrow, 1978. J

Miller, G. T., Jr. *Living in the Environment*. 2nd ed. Wadsworth, 1979. YA

Owen, Denis F. *What Is Ecology?* rev. Oxford University Press, 1979. YA

Parker, Sybil P., et al. *McGraw-Hill Encyclopedia of Environmental Science*. 2nd ed. McGraw-Hill, 1980. YA

Pope, Joyce. *A Closer Look at Jungles*. Watts/Gloucester, 1978. J

Pringle, Laurence. *What Shall We Do With the Land? Land Choices for America*. Crowell, 1981. J

ELECTRONICS

Augarten, Stan. *State of the Art*. Ticknor & Fields, 1983. YA

Edwards, John. *Exploring Electricity and Electronics with Projects*. Tab, 1983. YA

Markus, John. *Electronics Dictionary*. 4th ed. McGraw-Hill, 1978. YA

Mottershead, Allen. *Introduction to Electricity and Electronics*. Wiley, 1982. YA

Patrick, Dale R. *Electricity and Electronics*. Prentice-Hall, 1984. YA

Warring, Ronald H. *Understanding Electronics*. Tab, 1984. YA

ENERGY

Asimov, Isaac. *How Did We Find Out About Oil?* Walker, 1980. J

Asimov, Isaac. *How Did We Find Out About Solar Power?* Walker, 1981. J

Behrman, Daniel. *Solar Energy: The Awakening Science*. Little, Brown, 1980. YA

Bendick, Jeanne. *Putting the Sun to Work*. Garrard, 1979. J

Brown, Joseph E., and Anne Ensign. *Harness the Wind: The Story of Windmills*. Dodd, Mead, 1979. J

Davis, Bertha, and Whitfield, Susan. *The Coal Question*. Watts, 1982. YA

Dorf, Richard C. *The Energy Factbook*. McGraw-Hill, 1981. YA

Gabel, Medard. *Energy, Earth, and Everyone*. rev. Doubleday, 1980. YA

Goldin, Augusta R. *Geothermal Energy: A Hot Prospect*. Harcourt Brace Jovanovich, 1981. YA

Goldin, Augusta R. *Oceans of Energy: Reservoir of Power for the Future*. Harcourt Brace Jovanovich, 1980. YA

Halacy, Daniel Stephen. *Nuclear Energy*. Watts, 1978. J

Hyde, Margaret O. *Energy: The New Look*. McGraw-Hill, 1981. J

Kraft, Betsy Harvey. *Oil and Natural Gas*. rev. Watts, 1982. J

Lampton, Christopher. *Fusion: The Eternal Flame*. Watts, 1982. YA

Lauber, Patricia. *Tapping Earth's Heat*. Garrard, 1978. J

Smith, Norman F. *Wind Power*. Coward, McCann, 1981. J

LASERS

Hallmark, Clayton L. *Lasers: The Light Fantastic*. Tab, 1979. YA

Hecht, Jeff, and Teresi, Dick. *Laser: Supertool of the 1980s*. Ticknor & Fields, 1982. YA

Kettelkamp, Larry. *Lasers, the Miracle Light*. Morrow, 1979. J

Lewis, Bruce. *What Is a Laser?* Dodd, Mead, 1979. J

McKie, Robin. *Lasers*. Watts, 1983. J

MARINE BIOLOGY AND FISH

Abbott, R. Tucker. *Compendium of Seashells*. Dutton, 1982. YA

Amos, William H. *Wildlife of the Rivers*. Abrams, 1981. YA

Audubon Society Field Guide to North American Fishes, Whales, and Dolphins. Knopf, 1983. YA

Brown, Anne Ensign. *Wonders of Sea Horses*. Dodd, Mead, 1979. J

Carson, Rachel. *The Edge of the Sea*. Houghton Mifflin, 1979. YA

Cole, Joanna, and Wexler, Jerome. *A Fish Hatches*. Morrow, 1979. J

Cole, Sheila. *When the Tide Is Low*. Lothrop, 1985. J

Conklin, Gladys Plemon. *The Octopus and Other Cephalopods*. Holiday, 1977. J

Coulombe, Deborah A. *The Seaside Naturalist*. Prentice-Hall, 1984. YA

Freedman, Russell. *Killer Fish*. Holiday, 1982. J

Greenberg, Ida, and Jerry. *Sharks and Other Dangerous Sea Creatures*. Seahawk, 1981. YA

Jacobson, Morris K., and Franz, David R. *Wonders of Corals and Coral Reefs*. Dodd, Mead, 1979. J

McGowen, Tom. *Album of Sharks*. Rand McNally, 1977. J

Nelson, Joseph S. *Fishes of the World*. Wiley, 1984. YA

Oxford Scientific Films. *Jellyfish and Other Sea Creatures*. Putnam, 1982. J

Patent, Dorothy H. *Fish and How They Reproduce*. Holiday, 1978. J

Rotman, Jeffrey L. *Beneath Cold Seas*. Van Nostrand Reinhold, 1983. YA

Samson, John G. *The Pond*. Knopf, 1979. YA

MATHEMATICS

Adler, David A. *Roman Numerals*. Harper & Row/Crowell, 1977. J

Asimov, Isaac. *Realm of Algebra: A Guide to the Theory That Makes Sense of the Operations*. Houghton Mifflin, 1961; Fawcett, 1977. YA

Bitter, Gary G., and Metos, Thomas H. *Exploring with Pocket Calculators*. Messner, 1977. J

Carman, Robert A., and M. J. *Quick Arithmetic*. Wiley, 1974. YA

Coxeter, H. S., and Greitzer, S. L. *Geometry Revisited*. Random House, 1967; Mathematics Association, 1975. YA

Devi, Shakuntala. *Figuring: The Joy of Numbers*. Harper & Row, 1981. YA

Downing, Douglas. *Algebra, the Easy Way*. Barron's, 1983. YA

Drooyan, Irving, et al. *Essentials of Trigonometry*. 3rd ed. Macmillan, 1981. YA

Flegg, Graham. *Numbers*. Schocken, 1983. YA

Frankenstein, Marilyn. *Basic Algebra*. Prentice-Hall, 1979. YA

Gibson, Carol, ed. *The Facts on File Dictionary of Mathematics*. Facts on File, 1980. YA

Gowar, Norman. *An Invitation to Mathematics*. Oxford University Press, 1980. YA

Gullen, Michael. *Bridges to Infinity*. Tarcher, 1983. YA

Holton, Jean L. *Geometry: A New Way of Looking at Space*. Weybright & Talley, 1971. YA

Keedy, Mervin L., and Bittinger, Marvin L. *Arithmetic*. 3rd ed. Addison-Wesley, 1979. YA

Keedy, Mervin L., and Bittinger, Marvin L. *Introductory Algebra*. 3rd ed. Addison-Wesley, 1979. YA

McKeague, Charles P. *Elementary Algebra*. Academic Press, 1981. YA

Niven, Ivan, and Zuckerman, H. S. *An Introduction to the Theory of Numbers*. 4th ed. Wiley, 1980. YA

Pai, Hang Young. *The Complete Book of Chisanbop: Original Finger Calculation Method*. Van Nostrand Reinhold, 1981. J

Sitomer, Mindel, and Harry. *How Did Numbers Begin?* Harper & Row/Crowell, 1976. J

Streeter, James A. *Basic Mathematical Skills*. McGraw-Hill, 1984. YA

Tobey, John. *Beginning Algebra*. Prentice-Hall, 1984. YA

Watson, Clyde. *Binary Numbers*. Harper & Row/Crowell, 1977. J

MEDICINE

American Medical Association. *AMA Handbook of First Aid and Emergency Care*. Random House, 1980. YA

American Medical Association. *Family Medical Guide*. Random House, 1982. YA

Bennion, Lynn J. *Hypoglycemia*. Crown, 1983. YA
Berger, Melvin. *Germs Make Me Sick*. Harper & Row/Crowell, 1985. J
Berger, Melvin. *Medical Center Lab*. Day, 1976. J
Blau, Sheldon P. *Lupus, the Body Against Itself*. Doubleday, 1984. YA
Bruun, Ruth Dowling, and Bertil. *The Human Body*. Random House, 1982. J
Burns, Sheila L. *Allergies and You*. Messner, 1980. J
Doss, Helen Grigsby. *Your Skin Holds You In*. Messner, 1976. J
Gadd, Irna, and Laurence. *Arthritis Alternatives*. Facts on File, 1985. YA
Kapit, Wynn, and Elson, Lawrence. *Anatomy Coloring Book*. Harper & Row, 1977. YA
Linburg, Peter. *The Story of Your Heart*. Coward, McCann, 1979. J
Mangel, Charles. *Medicine*. Dial, 1984. YA
Margolies, Cynthia P. *Understanding Leukemia*. Scribner, 1983. YA
Miller, Jonathan. *The Body in Question*. Random House, 1979. YA
Miller, Jonathan. *The Human Body*. Viking/Studio, 1983. J
Nourse, Alan Edward. *Fractures, Dislocations, and Sprains*. Watts, 1978. J
Nourse, Alan Edward. *Your Immune System*. Watts, 1982. J
Pescar, Susan C. *Where Does It Hurt?* Facts on File, 1983. YA
Powell, Lenore S. *Alzheimer's Disease*. Addison-Wesley, 1983. YA
Silverstein, Alvin, and Virginia B. *Heartbeats: Your Body, Your Heart*. Lippincott; dist. by Harper & Row, 1983. J
Silverstein, Alvin, and Virginia B. *Runaway Sugar: All About Diabetes*. Lippincott; dist. by Harper & Row, 1981. J
Steinmann, Marion. *American Medical Association Guide to Backcare*. Random House, 1984. YA
Sydney, Sheldon B. *Ignore Your Teeth . . . and They'll Go Away*. Devida, 1982. YA
Ward, Brian R. *Body Maintenance*. Watts, 1983. J
Wilkin, Refna. *Dental Health*. Watts, 1976. J
Wilson, Ron. *How the Body Works*. Larousse, 1979. J

MENTAL HEALTH, PSYCHOLOGY

Applebaum, Stephen A. *Out in Inner Space*. Doubleday, 1979. YA
Arenson, Gloria. *Binge Eating*. Rawson, 1984. YA
Bugelski, Bergen Richard, and Graziano, Anthony M. *The Handbook of Practical Psychology*. Prentice-Hall, 1980. YA
Danton, Bruce L. *So You Want to See a Psychiatrist?* Arno, 1980. YA
Harris, Thomas A. *I'm OK—You're OK: A Practical Guide to Transactional Analysis*. Harper & Row, 1969; Avon, 1976. YA
Hyde, Margaret O. *Is This Kid Crazy? Understanding Unusual Behavior*. Westminster, 1983. J
Pope, Harrison. *New Hope for Binge Eaters*. Harper & Row, 1984. YA
Rubin, Theodore I. *Not to Worry*. Viking, 1984. YA

METEOROLOGY

Aylesworth, Thomas G. *Storm Alert: Understanding Weather Disasters*. Messner, 1980. YA
Branley, Franklyn M. *Flash, Crash, Rumble, and Roll*. Harper & Row/Crowell, 1985. J
Brindze, Ruth. *Hurricanes: Monster Storms from the Sea*. Atheneum, 1973. YA
Calder, Nigel. *The Weather Machine*. Viking, 1975; Penguin, 1977. YA
Dabbert, Walter. *Weather for Outdoorsmen*. Scribner, 1981. YA
Field, Frank. *Dr. Frank Field's Weather Book*. Putnam, 1981. YA
Gallant, Roy A. *Earth's Changing Climate*. Scholastic/Four Winds, 1979. YA
Lambert, David. *The Seasons*. Watts, 1983. J
Laycock, George. *Tornadoes: Killer Storms*. McKay, 1979. YA
Newton, James R. *Rain Shadow*. Harper & Row/Crowell, 1983. J
Ramsey, Dan. *How to Forecast Weather*. Tab, 1983. YA
Schaefer, Vincent J., and Day, John A. *A Field Guide to the Atmosphere*. Houghton Mifflin, 1981. YA
Tirado, Roberto. *Roberto Tirado's Weather Book*. Peregrine, 1981. YA

MICROSCOPE

Curry, Alan. *Under the Microscope*. Van Nostrand Reinhold, 1982. YA
Gillone, Lisa, and Gennaro, Joseph. *Small Worlds Close Up*. Crown, 1978. J
Klein, Aaron E. *The Electron Microscope: A Tool of Discovery*. McGraw-Hill, 1974. YA
Simon, Seymour. *Exploring with a Microscope*. Random House, 1969. J
Stehli, Georg. *The Microscope and How to Use It*. Sterling, 1961; Dover, 1970. YA

MINERALOGY

Dietrich, Richard V. *Minerals, Rocks, and Fossils*. Wiley, 1983. YA
Dietrich, Richard V. *Stones: Their Collection, Identification, and Uses*. Freeman, 1980. YA
McGowen, Tom. *Album of Rocks and Minerals*. Rand McNally, 1981. J
Mitchell, Richard S. *Mineral Names: What Do They Mean?* Van Nostrand Reinhold, 1979. YA
Pouch, Frederick H. *A Field Guide to Rocks and Minerals*. 4th ed. Houghton Mifflin, 1976. YA
Shedenhelm, W. R. C. *The Young Rockhound's Handbook*. Putnam, 1978. J
Webster, Ruth. *Gemologists' Compendium*. 6th ed. Van Nostrand Reinhold, 1976. YA

OCEANOGRAPHY

Barton, Robert. *The Oceans*. Facts on File, 1980. YA
Cook, Jan Leslie. *The Mysterious Undersea World*. National Geographic Society, 1980. J
Cousteau, Jacques-Yves, and Diolé, Philippe. *The Undersea Discoveries of Jacques-Yves Cousteau*. 8 vol. Doubleday, 1971–1973. YA
Groves, Donald G., and Hunt, Lee M. *Ocean World Encyclopedia*. McGraw-Hill, 1980. YA
Hendrickson, Robert. *The Ocean Almanac*. Doubleday, 1984. YA
Lambert, David. *The Oceans*. Watts/Warwick, 1980. J
Poynter, Margaret, and Collins, Donald. *Under the High Seas: New Frontiers in Oceanography*. Atheneum, 1983. J
The Rand McNally Atlas of the Oceans. Rand McNally, 1977. YA
Russell, Solveig Paulson. *What's Under the Sea?* Abingdon, 1982. J
Thorndike, Joseph, ed. *Mysteries of the Deep*. American Heritage, 1981. YA

PALEONTOLOGY AND DINOSAURS

Aliki. *Wild and Wooly Mammoths*. Harper & Row/Crowell, 1977. J
British Museum of Natural History. *Dinosaurs and Their Living Relatives*. Cambridge University Press, 1983. YA
Charig, Alan. *A New Look at Dinosaurs*. Facts on File, 1983. YA
Cobb, Vicki. *The Monsters Who Died: A Mystery About Dinosaurs*. Coward, McCann, 1983. J
Colbert, Edwin H. *Dinosaurs, An Illustrated History*. Hammond, 1983. YA
Freedman, Russell. *Dinosaurs and Their Young*. Holiday, 1983. J
Kaufmann, John. *Flying Reptiles: In the Age of the Dinosaurs*. Morrow, 1976. J
Lampton, Christopher. *Dinosaurs and the Age of Reptiles*. Watts, 1983. J
Pringle, Laurence P. *Dinosaurs and People: Fossils, Facts, and Fantasies*. Harcourt Brace Jovanovich, 1978. J
Sattler, Helen Roney. *Dinosaurs of North America*. Lothrop, 1981. J
Selsam, Millicent E. *Sea Monsters of Long Ago*. Scholastic/Four Winds, 1978. J
Selsam, Millicent E., and Hunt, Joyce. *A First Look at Dinosaurs*. Walker, 1982. J
Service, William. *The Dinosaurs: A Fantastic New View of a Lost Era*. Bantam, 1981. YA

PHYSICS

Adler, Irving. *Hot and Cold*. rev. Day, 1975. YA
Apfel, Necia H. *It's All Relative: Einstein's Theory of Relativity*. Lothrop, 1981. YA
Asimov, Isaac. *Asimov on Physics*. Doubleday, 1976. YA
Asimov, Isaac. *The Measure of the Universe*. Harper & Row, 1983. YA
Branley, Franklyn M. *Color: From Rainbows to Lasers*. Harper & Row/Crowell, 1978. YA
Davies, Paul. *Other Worlds*. Simon & Schuster, 1981. YA
Kavaler, Lucy. *A Matter of Degree: Heat, Life, and Death*. Harper & Row, 1981. YA
Knight, David C. *Silent Sound: The World of Ultrasonics*. Morrow 1980. J
Landau, L. D., and Kitaigorodsky, A. I. *Physics for Everyone: Motion, Heat*. Imported, 1979. YA
Lefkowitz, R. J. *Forces in the Earth: A Book About Gravity and Magnetism*. Parents' Magazine Press, 1976. J
Lerner, Rita G., and Trigg, George L., eds. *Encyclopedia of Physics*. Addison-Wesley, 1981. YA
Mendelssohn, K. *The Quest for Absolute Zero: The Meaning of Low-Temperature Physics*. rev. McGraw-Hill, 1977. YA
Morris, Richard. *Light*. Bobbs-Merrill, 1979. YA
Pagels, Heinz R. *The Cosmic Code: Physics as the Language of Nature*. Simon & Schuster, 1982. YA

Pringle, Laurence. *Radiation: Waves and Particles*. Enslow, 1983. YA

Segre, Emilio. *From X-rays to Quarks: Modern Physicists and Their Discoveries*. Freeman, 1980. YA

Selsam, Millicent E. *Up, Down, and Around: The Force of Gravity*. Doubleday, 1977. J

Simon, Seymour. *Shadow Magic*. Lothrop, 1985. J

Snow, C. P. *The Physicists*. Little, Brown, 1981. YA

Swartz, Clifford E. *Phenomenal Physics*. Wiley, 1981. YA

Taffel, Alexander. *Physics: Its Methods and Meanings*. Allyn & Bacon, 1981. YA

Weiss, Harvey. *Machines and How They Work*. Harper & Row/Crowell, 1983. J

Wilson, David. *The Colder the Better*. Atheneum, 1980. YA

Wolf, Fred. *Taking the Quantum Leap: The New Physics for Nonscientists*. Harper & Row, 1981. YA

REPRODUCTION AND PREGNANCY

Bell, Ruth, et al. *Changing Bodies, Changing Lives: A Book for Teens on Sex and Relationships*. Random House, 1981. YA

Boston Women's Health Book Collective. *Ourselves and Our Children*. Random House, 1978. YA

Gardner-Loulan, JoAnn, et al. *Period*. My Mama's Press, 1979. YA

Jessel, Camilla. *The Joy of Birth: A Book for Parents and Children*. Dutton/Hillside, 1983. J

Nourse, Alan Edward. *Menstruation: Just Plain Talk*. Watts, 1980. J

Parker, Stephen, and Bavosi, John. *Life Before Birth: The Story of the First Nine Months*. Cambridge University Press, 1979. J

Ward, Brian R. *Birth and Growth*. Watts, 1983. J

SPACE TRAVEL

Adelman, Saul J., and Benjamin. *Bound for the Stars*. Prentice-Hall, 1980. YA

Armstrong, Neil, et al. *First on the Moon*. Little, Brown, 1970. YA

Baker, David. *The History of Manned Space Flight*. Crown, 1982. YA

Blumberg, Rhoda. *The First Travel Guide to the Moon: What to Pack, How to Go, and What to See When You Get There*. Scholastic/Four Winds, 1980. J

Branley, Franklyn M. *Columbia and Beyond: The Story of the Space Shuttle*. Collins, 1979. YA

Fichter, George S. *The Space Shuttle*. Watts, 1981. J

Grey, Jerry. *Beachheads in Space*. Macmillan, 1983. YA

Oberg, James E. *The New Race for Space*. Stackpole, 1984. YA

O'Leary, Brian. *Project Space Station*. Stackpole, 1982. YA

SUBSTANCE ABUSE

Berger, Gilda. *Addiction: Its Causes, Problems, and Treatments*. Watts, 1982. YA

Burton, Dee, and Wohl, Gary. *The Joy of Quitting*. Macmillan, 1977. YA

Gordon, Barbara. *I'm Dancing as Fast as I Can*. Harper & Row, 1979. YA

Hyde, Margaret O. *Know About Alcohol*. McGraw-Hill, 1978. J

Hyde, Margaret O. *Know About Smoking*. McGraw-Hill, 1983. J

Hyde, Margaret O., et al. *Mind Drugs*. McGraw-Hill, 1981. YA

Latimer, Dean, and Goldberg, Jeff. *Flowers in the Blood: The Story of Opium*. Watts, 1981. YA

Luks, Allan. *Will America Sober Up?* Beacon, 1983. YA

Mothner, Ira. *How to Get Off Drugs*. Rolling Stone, 1984. YA

Seixas, Judith S. *Alcohol—What It Is, What It Does*. Greenwillow/Morrow, 1977. J

Silverstein, Alvin, and Virginia B. *Alcoholism*. Lippincott, 1975. YA

TECHNOLOGY AND INVENTIONS

DeBono, Edward, ed. *Eureka!* Holt, Rinehart & Winston, 1974, 1979. YA

Fuller, R. Buckminster. *Inventions*. St. Martin's Press, 1983. YA

How Things Work. National Geographic Society, 1983. J

Lodewijk, T., et al. *The Way Things Work: An Illustrated Encyclopedia of Technology*. 2 vols. Simon & Schuster, 1967–1979. YA. 1 vol. ed. for young readers, 1973. J

MacCracken, Calvin D. *A Handbook for Inventors*. Scribner, 1983. YA

Sandak, Cass R. *Bridges*. Watts, 1983. J

Sandak, Cass R. *Canals*. Watts, 1983. J

Sandak, Cass R. *Dams*. Watts, 1983. J

Silverstein, Alvin, and Virginia B. *Future Life: The Biotechnology Revolution*. Prentice-Hall, 1982. YA

Silverstein, Alvin, and Virginia B. *The World of Bionics*. Methuen, 1979. YA

Strandh, Sigvard. *A History of the Machine*. A & W, 1979. YA

Toffler, Alvin. *Future Shock*. Random House, 1970. YA

Toffler, Alvin. *The Third Wave*. Morrow, 1980; Bantam, 1981. YA

TIME

Burns, Marilyn. *This Book Is About Time*. Little, Brown, 1978. J

Gibbons, Gail. *Clocks and How They Go*. Harper & Row/Crowell, 1979. J

Howse, Derek. *Greenwich Time and the Discovery of the Longitude*. Oxford University Press, 1980. YA

Jespersen, James, and Fitz-Randolph, Jane. *Time and Clocks for the Space Age*. Atheneum, 1979. YA

Schneider, Herman. *How Scientists Find Out About Matter, Time, Space, Energy*. McGraw-Hill, 1976. YA

Trivett, Daphne, and John. *Time for Clocks*. Harper & Row/Crowell, 1979. J

TRANSPORTATION

Ball, Don. *America's Railroads: The Second Generation*. Norton, 1980. YA

Bobrick, Benson. *Labyrinths of Iron: A History of the World's Subways*. Newsweek, 1981. YA

Cole, Joanna. *Cars and How They Go*. Harper & Row/Crowell, 1983. J

Crouch, Tom D. *The Eagle Aloft*. Smithsonian Institution Press, 1983. YA

DuJonchay, Yvan. *The Handbook of World Transportation*. Facts on File, 1978. YA

Hindley, Geoffrey. *A History of Roads*. Citadel, 1972, 1977. YA

Hollingsworth, Brian. *Atlas of the World's Railways*. Everest, 1983. YA

Mrazek, James E., Jr. *Ultralights*. St. Martin's Press, 1982. YA

Nock, O. S. *Railways of the USA*. Hastings, 1979. YA

Olney, Ross Robert. *The Internal Combustion Engine*. Lippincott, dist. Harper & Row, 1982. J

The Rand McNally Encyclopedia of Transportation. Rand McNally, 1976. YA

Ridgely-Nevitt, Cedric. *American Steamships on the Atlantic*. Delaware, 1981. YA

Serling, Robert J. *The Jet Age*. Time-Life Books, 1982. YA

Solberg, Carl. *Conquest of the Skies*. Little, Brown, 1979. YA

Wall, Robert. *Ocean Liners*. Collins, 1978. YA

ZOOLOGY

Allen, Thomas B. *Earth's Amazing Animals*. National Wildlife Federation, 1983. YA

Black, Hallie. *Animal Cooperation: A Look at Sociobiology*. Morrow, 1981. YA

Crump, Donald J., et al., eds. *National Geographic Book of Mammals*. 2 vols. National Geographic Society, 1981. J

Dixon, Dougal. *After Man*. St. Martin's Press, 1981. YA

Freedman, Russell. *Tooth and Claw: A Look at Animal Weapons*. Holiday, 1980. J

Grizmek, Bernhard, ed. *Animal Life Encyclopedia*. 13 vols. Van Nostrand Reinhold, 1972–1975. YA

Hartman, Jane E. *How Animals Care for Their Young*. Holiday, 1980. YA

Headstrom, Richard. *Identifying Animal Tracks*. Dover, 1983. YA

Kohl, Judith, and Herbert. *Pack, Band, and Colony: The World of Social Animals*. Farrar, Straus & Giroux, 1983. J

Komori, Atsushi. *Animal Mothers*. Philomel, 1983. J

Napier, Prue, et al. *Elephants and Other Land Giants*. Time-Life Films; dist. by Little, Brown, 1977. J

Nussbaum, Hedda. *Animals Build Amazing Homes*. Random House, 1979. J

Patent, Dorothy H. *Hunters and the Hunted: Surviving in the Animal World*. Holiday, 1981. J

Selsam, Millicent E., and Hunt, Joyce. *A First Look at Animals Without Backbones*. Walker, 1977. J

Selsam, Millicent E., and Hunt, Joyce. *A First Look at Whales*. Walker, 1980. J

Whitfield, Philip, ed. *Macmillan Illustrated Animal Encyclopedia*. Macmillan, 1984. YA

Zim, Herbert S., et al. *Zoology*. Western, 1958. YA

INDEX

This index makes it easy for you to find any subject in the encyclopedia. The subject name is followed by a number which tells you the page of the subject. An *italic number* is the page of an illustration of the subject. A subject that is in all CAPITAL LETTERS refers to a main entry in the encyclopedia. The page numbers immediately following tell you where the entry is. Other page numbers tell you where the subject is mentioned in other entries. For example: ENGINE 560-564, *563;* 123-124. This means that you will find an entry on engines on pages 560 through 564 and a picture on page 563. Another mention of engine is on pages 123 and 124. If a subject is not in all capital letters (for example: Alphabet 355), it means that there is no entry on the subject in the encyclopedia but that the subject is mentioned in another entry on the page indicated.

A

AARDVARK 1, *1*
AARDWOLF 1, *1*
ABACUS 1-2, *2*
ABALONE 2, *2*
ABDOMEN 2; 848
ABERRATION 2-3, *3;* 1191
Ablative shield 771
Abnormal psychology 1370
ABO system 187
ABORTION 3
A-bomb 1163-1164
ABRASIVE 3-5, *4*
Absolute humidity 809
Absolute magnitude 992
ABSOLUTE ZERO 5; 399-400
ABSORPTION AND ADSORPTION 5-6, *6*
Absorption refrigerator 1427-1428
AC generator 701-702
ACCELERATION 6-7; 743-744
ACCELERATORS, PARTICLE 8-10, *8, 9*
ACCOMMODATION 10, *10*
Acetate 10
ACETIC ACID 10
ACETONE 10-11
ACETYLENE 11, *11*
ACHILLES TENDON 11-12, *11*
ACID 12-14, *12, 13, 14*
ACNE 14
ACOUSTICS 14-17, *15, 16*
ACROMEGALY 17; 194
ACRYLIC 17-18, *17*
ACTINIUM 18
ADAPTATION 18-19, *18, 19*
ADDER 19, *19*
ADDICTION 19-20
Addiction, drug 479
ADDISON'S DISEASE 20
Addition 94
Additive color mixing 349
ADENOID 20, *20*
ADHESION 20, *21*
ADHESIVE 20-21, *21*
ADLER, ALFRED 21-22
ADOLESCENCE 22
ADP 118
ADRENAL GLANDS 22-23, *22;* 800
Adsorption chromatography 311
Adult 850
Adventitious root 1465-1466
Aedes 1110
Aerial photography 1004
AEROBE 23
AERODYNAMICS 23-25, *23, 24, 25*
AERONAUTICS 25-26; 107
AEROSOL 26, *26*
AEROSPACE 26

African elephant 549
African rhinoceros 1445
African wild ass 103
AGASSIZ, LOUIS 26-27, *27*
AGATE 27, *27*
AGAVE 27-28, *27*
AGGLOMERATE 28
AGRICULTURE 28-30, *29*
AGRONOMY 30
AHF 778-779
A-horizon 1561
AIDS 1773
Aiken, Howard H. 361
AILANTHUS 30
AIR 30-32, *31, 32;* 112
AIR MASS 33-34
Air pollution 31-32; 1316-1317
Air pressure 1814
Air-conduction hearing aid 765
AIR-CUSHION VEHICLE 32-33, *32;* 1101
AIRPLANE 34-37, *35, 36, 37*
Airplane propeller 1357
AIRPORT 37-39
Alaska king crab 390
ALBATROSS 39
ALBINO 39, *39*
ALCHEMY 39-40; 296-297
ALCOHOL 40-41, *40*
ALCOHOLISM 41
ALDEHYDE 41
ALDER 41
Aldrin, Edwin 1355
ALEWIFE 41-42
ALFALFA 42
ALGAE 42-43, *43*
ALGEBRA 44-46, *44, 45*
ALGOL 1062
ALIMENTARY CANAL 46, *46*
Aliphatic hydrocarbon 818
ALKALI 46-47, *47*
ALKALI METAL 47
ALKALINE EARTH METAL 47
ALKALOID 47-48
Allergens 48
ALLERGY 48
ALLIGATOR 48
ALLOTROPE 48-49
ALLOY 49-51, *49, 50*
ALLUVIUM 51
ALMOND 51
ALOE 51
ALPHA CENTAURI 51-52
ALPHA PARTICLE 52
Alphabet 355
Alpide belt 496
ALTERNATING CURRENT 52; 405-406
ALTERNATION OF GENERATIONS 52-53, *53*
ALTIMETER 53, *53*
ALTITUDE 53
ALUM 53-54

ALUMINUM 54-55, *54, 55*
AM 1394
AMALGAM 55
AMARANTH FAMILY 55-56, *55*
AMARYLLIS FAMILY 56, *56*
AMBER 56
AMEBA 56-57, *56*
Amebic dysentery 489
AMERICIUM 57
AMETHYST 57
AMINE 57
AMINO ACID 57-58
AMMETER 58
AMMONIA 58-59, *58*
AMMONITE 59, *59*
Ammonium sulfate 59
AMPERE 59
AMPÈRE, ANDRÉ 59-60, *60;* 518
AMPHETAMINE 60
AMPHIBIAN 60-62, *61*
AMPLIFIER 62, *62;* 790
AMPLITUDE 62-63, *63;* 1577; 1809
Amplitude modulation 1394
ANACONDA 63, *63*
ANAEROBE 63-64
ANALGESIC 64; 478
Analog computer 362
Anaphase 1088
ANATOMY 64-65, *64;* 175
ANCHOVY 65
Anders, William 1354
ANDREWS, ROY CHAPMAN 65
ANDROID 65-66
ANDROMEDA 66, *66*
Andromeda Nebula 66
ANEMIA 66-67; 308
ANEMOMETER 67, *67*
Aneroid barometer 148
ANESTHETIC 67, *67;* 478
ANGELFISH 67-68, *68*
ANGIOSPERM 68, *68;* 1252, 1293-1294
ANGSTROM UNIT 69
ANHYDRIDE 69
ANILINE 69
Animal breeding 206-207
ANIMAL KINGDOM 69-71, *70-71;* 319
Animal parasite 1219
Animal tissue 1717
Animated film 1114
ANION 72; 870-871
ANNEAL 72
Annealing 773
ANNELIDA 72, *72*
ANNUAL PLANT 72
ANNUAL RING 73, *73*
ANODIZING 73
Anopheles 1110
ANT 73-74
ANT LION 84, *84*
ANTBIRD 74
ANTEATER 74, *74*

ANTELOPE 74-75
Antelope kangaroo 889
ANTENNA 75, *75*
ANTENNAE 76, *76*
ANTHER 76
ANTHERIDIUM 76
Anthracite 336
ANTHROPOID 76-77, *76;* 1342
ANTHROPOLOGY 77
ANTIBIOTICS 77-79, *78, 79;* 477
ANTIBODY 79-80; 836-837
ANTICLINE 80-81, *80*
ANTICYCLONE 81, *81*
ANTIFREEZE 81-82
Antigen 187
ANTIMATTER 82, *82*
ANTIMONY 82
Antiparticle 82; 1223
ANTISEPTIC 83
Antiserum 477; 1513
ANTITOXIN 83; 836
ANTLER 83-84, *83*
Anuran 62, *61*
ANUS 84
AORTA 84; 766-767
APATITE 84-85
APE 85; 808
Aperture 234
APHID 85, *85*
Apodan 62, *61*
APOPLEXY 85
Appendicular skeleton 1539
APPENDIX 86
APPLE 86, *86*
Applied mathematics 1017
Applied science 1498
APRICOT 86
AQUARIUM 86
AQUARIUS 87
AQUATIC PLANT 87, *87*
AQUEDUCT 87-88
Aquifer 98
AQUILA 88
ARACHNID 88, *88*
ARBORETUM 88-89
ARBORVITAE 89
Arc furnace 678
ARC, ELECTRIC 89
Arch bridge 207
ARCHAEOPTERYX 89, *89*
ARCHEGONIUM 89-90, *90*
Archeologist 90, *91*
ARCHEOLOGY 90-91
ARCHEOZOIC ERA 91
ARCHERFISH 91, *91*
ARCHIMEDES 91-92; 1018
Archimedes' principle 92
Archimedean screw *92*
Architectural acoustics 14-17
Archosauria 451
ARGO 92

ARGON 92; 1155
ARIES 93 ·
ARISTOTLE 93, *93*
ARITHMETIC 93-95, *93*, *94*, *95*
ARMADILLO 95-96, *96*
Armature 523, 524
ARMSTRONG, NEIL ALDEN 96, *96*; 1353
AROMATIC AND ALIPHATIC COMPOUNDS 96
Aromatic hydrocarbon 818
ARRHENIUS, SVANTE 97
ARROW WORM 97, *97*
ARSENIC 97
Arteriolar sclerosis 97
ARTERIOSCLEROSIS 97-98
ARTERY 98
ARTESIAN WELL 98, *98*
ARTHRITIS 98-99
ARTHROPODA 99-100, *99*
ARTICHOKE 100
Artificial diamond 441
Artificial element 546
Artificial immunity 837
Artificial insemination 207
Artificial satellite 1485-1486
Artificial vegetative propagation 1772
ARUM FAMILY 100, *100*
ASBESTOS 100-101
ASCHELMINTHES 101
ASEPSIS 101
ASEXUAL REPRODUCTION 101-102; 1431
ASH 102, *102*
Ash, volcanic 1787
Asian elephant 549
Asian rhinoceros 1445
Asiatic black bear 183
ASPARAGUS 102
ASPHALT 102
ASS 103
ASSAYING 103
Assembly line 122-123
Association colloid 347
ASTATINE 103
ASTER 103
ASTEROID 103-104, *104*; 1568
ASTHMA 104
Astigmatism 3; 928
ASTROLABE 104
ASTROLOGY 104-105
ASTRONAUTICS 105-107, *105*, *106*
Astronomer 107-108, 110
ASTRONOMICAL UNIT 107
ASTRONOMY 107-110, *108*, *109*, *110*
ASTROPHYSICS 110-112, *111*, 109
Atherosclerosis 97
ATMOSPHERE 112-114, *112*, *113*; 494
ATMOSPHERE (UNIT) 114
Atmospheric pressure 114, 191-192
ATOLL 115, *114*
ATOM 115-117, *116*, *117*
Atomic bomb 1163
Atomic clock 313
Atomic energy 117
Atomic furnace 678
ATOMIC NUMBER 117-118
Atomic structure 543
ATOMIC WEIGHT 118; 1092
ATP 118
Attack submarine 1638
AUDUBON, JOHN JAMES 118
Auger 474

AUK 118-119, *119*
AURIGA 119
AURORA 119, *119*
Aurora australis 119
Aurora borealis 119
AUSTRALOID 119-120; 808
AUTOMATION 120-122, *120*, *121*; 1677-1678
AUTOMOBILE 122-125, *123*, *124*
Automobile safety 125
Autonomic nervous system 1144
Autopsy 1227
Auxin 798
AVALANCHE 125
AVIATION, HISTORY OF 125-130, *127-128*, *129*, *130*
AVOCADO 130
AVOCET 130-131, *130*
Avogadro's law *691*
AVOGADRO, AMEDEO 131
Axial skeleton 1539
AXIL 131
Azide 1152
AZIMUTH 131

B

BABBAGE, CHARLES 131; 361
BABOON 131, *132*
Babylonian calendar 228
BABYLONIAN CIVILIZATION 131, *133*
Bacillary dysentery 489
Bacillus 135
BACKSWIMMER 133-134, *134*
BACON, FRANCIS 134
BACTERIA 134-136, *134*, *135*, *136*; 454
BACTERIOPHAGE 136-137
BADGER 137, *137*
BAEKELAND, LEO 137
BAER, KARL ERNST VON 137
BAKELITE 137-138; 1299
BALANCE 138, *138*
BALD EAGLE 138-139, *139*
Ball bearing 154
Ball lightning 944
BALLISTICS 139-140, *140*
BALLOON 141-143, *141*, *142*
BALSAM 143
BAMBOO 143
BANANA 143-144, *144*
BANDICOOT 144, *144*
BANTING, SIR FREDERICK GRANT 144; 856-857
BANYAN 144-145
BARBERRY FAMILY 145
BARBITURATE 145
BARIUM 145-146
BARK 146; 1735
BARLEY 146, *146*
BARNACLE 146-147, *147*
BARNARD, CHRISTIAAN NEETHLING 147
Barograph 148
BAROMETER 147-148, *147*, *148*
BARRACUDA 148
BASALT 148-149, *149*
BASE 149-150
BASIC 365; 1062
BASIDIUM 150
BASKET STAR 150, *150*
BASS 150
BAT 150-151, *151*
BATHOLITH 151
BATHYSPHERE AND BATHYSCAPHE 151-152, *151*

Batt insulation 854
BATTERY 152-153, *152*
Bauxite 54
BAYBERRY 153
BEADLE, GEORGE WELLS 153
Beam bridge 207, 208, 209
BEAN 153-154, *154*
BEAR 154
BEARING 154-155, *155*
BEATS 155
BEAUFORT SCALE 155, *156*
BEAVER 155-157, *156*
BECQUEREL, ANTOINE HENRI 157
BEDBUG 157, *157*
BEE 157-160, *158*, *159*
BEECH FAMILY 160, *160*
Beef cattle 260
Beefalo 181-182
BEETLE 160-161, *160*, *161*
BEGONIA 161
BEHAVIOR OF ANIMALS 162-163, *162*, *163*
Behavioral therapy 1368
BÉKÉSY, GEORG VON 163
BELEMNITE 163
BELL, ALEXANDER GRAHAM 163-164; 356; 765-766; 1681-1682
Bennet, Abraham 539
BENTHOS 164, *164*
BENZ, KARL 164
BENZENE 164-165, *165*; 96
Benzol 164-165
BERIBERI 165
BERKELIUM 165
BERNOULLI FAMILY 165-166
Bernoulli, Daniel 166; 634
Bernoulli, Jacques 165
Bernoulli, Jean 165-166
BERNOULLI'S EFFECT 166, *166*
BERRY 166, *166*
BERYL 166-167, *167*
BERYLLIUM 167
BERZELIUS, JÖNS JAKOB 167
Bessemer process 1622
BESSEMER, SIR HENRY 167
Best, Charles 856-857
Beta blocker 768
BETA PARTICLE 167-168
BETELGEUSE 168
B-horizon 1561
BICEPS 168
BIENNIAL PLANT 168
Big bang theory 385, *385*
BIG DIPPER AND LITTLE DIPPER 168
BILHARZIA 168
BIMETALLIC STRIP 168-169
Bimetallic strip thermometer 1703-1704
Binary fission 101
BINARY NUMBERS 169-170, *169*, *170*
BINDWEED FAMILY 171, *171*
BINET, ALFRED 171
Binet-Simon intelligence test 171
BINOCULARS 171-172, *171*
BIOCHEMISTRY 172-173, 175; 299
Biogeography 705-706
BIOLOGICAL CONTROL 173-174, *173*, *174*
Biological oceanography 1180
Biological psychology 175
BIOLOGICAL RHYTHM 174
BIOLOGY 175-176
BIOLUMINESCENCE 176
Biomathematics 175
Bionics 177

BIOPHYSICS 176-177, 175
BIOSPHERE 177
BIRCHES 177-178, *177*
BIRD 178-181, *178*, *179*, *180*, *181*
Birth control 374
BISMUTH 181
BISON 181-182, *182*; 213
BIVALVE 182, *182*, *183*
BLACK BEAR 183, *183*
BLACK HOLE 183-185, *184*
BLACK LIGHT 185
Black rat 1416
Black tea 1674
BLACK WIDOW 185, *185*
BLACKBIRD 183
Blade 919
Blanket insulation 855
Blast furnace 677-678
Blight 675
Block diagram 1616
BLOOD 185-187, *186*
BLOOD GROUPS 187-188, *187*
Blood pressure 186-187
BLOOD TRANSFUSION 188-189, *188*
Blow molding 1301
Blue crab 390
BLUE JAY 189
BLUE WHALE 189-190, *189*
BLUEBIRD 189
BOA 190, *190*
Boa constrictor 190
Boat bug 133
BOBCAT 190-191
BOBOLINK 191
Body membrane 1032
BOHR, NIELS 191, *191*; 1381-1382
BOILING AND BOILING POINT 191-192, *191*, *192*
BOLL WEEVIL 192, *192*
BOLLWORM 192
BOND, CHEMICAL 193
BONE 193-194, *193*, *194*
Bone-conduction hearing aid 765
BORAGE FAMILY 194, *194*
BORAX 194-195, *195*
Boring 474
Borman, Frank 1354
BORON 195-196
Borosilicate glass 724
BOTANY 196, *196*; 175
BOTULISM 197
BOUGAINVILLEA 197
BOWERBIRD 197, *197*
BOWFIN 197-198, *198*
Box caisson 223
BOX ELDER 198
BOYLE, ROBERT 198, *198*; 297
BOYLE'S LAW 198-199; *691*
BRACHIOPOD 199
Bract 921
BRAGG FAMILY 199
Bragg, Sir William Henry 199
Bragg, Sir William Lawrence 199
BRAHE, TYCHO 199-200, *199*; 108, 109, *108*
BRAIN 200-202, *201*; 1143
Brain stem 202
BRAKE 202-203, *202*
Braking system 124-125
BRASS 203, *203*
Brass instrument 1579
BRASSICA 203-204, *203*
BRAUN, WERNHER VON 204-205, *204*
BRAZIL NUT 205
Brazing *1570-1571*
Breast cancer 241
Breathing 1443-1444
BREEDING 205-207, *205*, *206*

BRIDGE 207-209, *207*, *208*, *209*
Brightness 350
BRINE 209
BRISTLETAIL 209-210, *210*
BRITISH THERMAL UNIT 210
BRITTLE STAR 210, *210*
Broadleaf tree 1734, 1735
BROMINE 210
Bronchial asthma 104
BRONZE 210-211, *211*
BROWN BEAR 211-212, *211*
Brown rat 1416
BROWNIAN MOVEMENT 212
Bubble chamber 10, *9*
BUCKTHORN FAMILY 212
BUCKWHEAT FAMILY 212
BUD 212-213
BUDDING 213, *213*; 101
BUFFALO 213; 181-182
BUG 213
BUILDING CONSTRUCTION
    213-215, *214*
BULB AND CORM 215, *215*
BULLFROG 216, *216*
Bumblebee 158
BUNSEN BURNER 216, *216*
BURBANK, LUTHER 216-217
BURETTE 217
Bush, Vannevar 361
Bushnell, David 1638-1639
BUTANE 217
BUTTERCUP 217, *217*
BUTTERFLY AND MOTH 218-220,
    219
BUZZARD 220
BYRD, RICHARD E. 220

C

CABBAGE 220-221
CABLE 221
Cable television 1689
CACAO 221
CACOMISTLE 221-222
CACTUS FAMILY 222, *222*
CADDIS FLY 222
CADMIUM 222-223
CAIMAN 223
CAISSON 223, *223*
CAISSON DISEASE 223-224
CALCITE 224
CALCIUM 224
CALCIUM CARBONATE 224-225,
    225
CALCIUM CHLORIDE 225
CALCULATOR 225-227, *226*
CALCULUS 227, *227*; 1018
CALENDAR 227-229
Calendar, religious 228-229
CALIBRATION 229
CALIFORNIUM 229
CALIPER, MEASURING 229-230,
    229
CALORIE 230
CALYX 230, *230*
CAM 230-231, *230*
CAMBIUM 231
CAMBRIAN PERIOD 231-232, *231*
CAMEL 232-233, *232*
CAMERA 233-237, *234*, *235*, *236*
Camera obscura 233
CAMOUFLAGE 237-238, *238*
CANAL 238-240, *239*, *240*
CANARY 240, *240*
CANCER (CONSTELLATION)
    240-241
CANCER (DISEASE) 241-242, *241*
CANDELA 242

Candle clock 328
CANIS MAJOR AND CANIS
    MINOR 242
Canning 645-646
CANTILEVER 242
Cantilever bridge 209
CANYON 242-243, *243*
Capacitor 244
CAPACITOR AND CAPACITANCE
    243-244, *244*
CAPILLARY ACTION 244
Capoid 808
CAPRICORNUS 244-245
CARAT 245
CARBOHYDRATE 245; 444; 1173
CARBON 245-247, *246*; 118
CARBON CYCLE 247, *247*
CARBON DIOXIDE 247-248
CARBON MONOXIDE 248-249
Carbon steel 1620, 1622
CARBONIFEROUS PERIOD 248
CARBURETOR 249; 562
Cardiac muscle 1122-1123
CARDINAL 249-250
Cardiovascular drug 478
CARIBOU 250
CARIES 250
CARNEGIE, ANDREW 250-251
CARNIVORE 251, *251*
CARNIVOROUS PLANTS 251-252,
    252
CARNOT, NICOLAS LÉONARD S.
    252
CAROTENE 252
CARP 252, *252*
CARROT 252-253
CARTILAGE 253
CARTOGRAPHY 253
CARVER, GEORGE
    WASHINGTON 253
CASE HARDENING 254
CASE-BEARER MOTH 253-254
CASEIN 254
CASSAVA 254
Cassette tape recorder 1668
CAST IRON 255-256; 872
CASTING 254-255, *254*
CAT 256, *256*
CATALPA 256
CATALYST 257
Catalytic cracking 390
CATERPILLAR 257-258
CATFISH 258, *258*
CATHODE RAY 258
CATHODE-RAY TUBE 258-259,
    258; 533
Cation 870-871
CATKIN 259, *259*
CATTLE 259-260, *260*
Caucasoid 808
CAVE 260-262, *261*, *262*
CAVENDISH, HENRY 262; 1152
CAVITATION 263
Cayley, Sir George 126
CEDAR 263
CELERY 263
Celestial navigation 1133
CELESTIAL SPHERE 263-264,
    263, *264*
CELL 265-268, *265*, *267*
Cell membrane 1030, 1031
CELL, ELECTRICAL 268-269, *269*
CELLOPHANE 269
Cellular respiration 1442
CELLULOID 269
CELLULOSE 269-270, 245
CELLULOSE ACETATE 270
Celsius 270
CELSIUS SCALE 270-271
CELSIUS, ANDERS 270

CEMENT AND CONCRETE 271-
    272, *272*
CENOZOIC ERA 272-273
CENTAURUS 273
CENTER OF GRAVITY 273, *273*
CENTIMETER-GRAM-SECOND
    SYSTEM 274
CENTIPEDE 274, *274*
CENTRAL HEATING 274-276, *275*
Central nervous system 1143
Centrifugal force 276-277
Centrifugal pump 1376
CENTRIFUGE 276, *276*
CENTRIPETAL FORCE 276-277,
    277
CEPHALOPOD 277-278, *277*
CEPHEUS 278, *278*
CERAMICS 278-279, *279*
CEREAL CROP 279-280, *279*, *280*
Cereal grass 741
CEREBELLUM 280, 200
CEREBRUM 280, 200
Ceres 103, 109
CERIUM 280-281
CESIUM 281
CHADWICK, SIR JAMES 281;
    1222
Chaffee, Roger 1354
Chain lightning 944
CHAIN REACTION 282-283, *282*;
    1160-1161
CHAIN, ERNST BORIS 281-282;
    1236
CHALK 283, *283*
CHAMELEON 283, *283*
CHAMOIS 283-284
CHARCOAL 284, *284*
CHARGE 284-285
Charging, electrostatic 541-542
CHARLES' LAW 285; 691
CHEETAH 285, *285*
CHEMICAL ANALYSIS 286-287,
    287
CHEMICAL AND BIOLOGICAL
    WARFARE 287-288
Chemical bond 1093
Chemical catalyst 257
CHEMICAL COMBINATION,
    LAWS OF 288
Chemical engineering 567
Chemical equilibrium 1014
Chemical explosive 584
CHEMICAL FORMULAS AND
    EQUATIONS 288
CHEMICAL INDUSTRY 289-294,
    289, *290*, *291*
Chemical oceanography 1180
Chemical products 293-294
Chemical property 1021
CHEMICAL REACTION 294-296,
    295
Chemical waste 293
CHEMISTRY 296
CHEMISTRY, HISTORY OF
    296-299, *298*
Chemotherapy 241-242
Chemotropism 1118
CHERRY 299, *299*
Chest 1539
CHESTNUT 299-300, *300*
Chewing lice 933
CHICKEN POX 300
CHICKWEED 300
CHICORY 300-301, *301*
Chimney cooling tower 377
CHIMPANZEE 301-302, *302*
CHINCHILLA 303, *303*
CHINESE CIVILIZATION 303-304
CHIP 304-305, *304*; 1677
CHIPMUNK 305, *305*

CHITIN 305-306, *306*
CHITON 306, *306*
Chlamydia 1773
CHLORATE 306
CHLORDANE 306
CHLORIDE 306
Chlorination 1807
CHLORINE 306-307, *307*
CHLOROFORM 307
CHLOROPHYLL 307-308, *307*;
    921; 1263
CHLOROPLAST 312
CHLOROSIS 308
Choke 249
CHOLERA 308
CHOLESTEROL 308
CHORDATA 308-309, *309*; 807
C-horizon 1561
Choroid 591-592
Christy, James W. 1306
Chromatic aberration 3; 928
CHROMATOGRAPHY 309-311,
    310
CHROMIUM 311-312, *311*
CHROMOPLAST 312
CHROMOSOME 312, *312*; 578; 703
Chromosome mapping 784
Chromosphere 1649
CHRONOMETER 313
CHRYSANTHEMUM 313, *313*
CICADA 313-314, *314*
CICHLID 314, *314*
Ciliate 1364
CILIUM 314
Circle 713, 714
CIRCUIT BREAKER 316, *316*
CIRCUIT, ELECTRIC 315-316, *315*
Circular saw 984
CIRCULATORY SYSTEM 316-317,
    317
Circum-Pacific belt 496
Cirque 721
CIRRHOSIS 317
CITRIC ACID 317
CITRUS FRUIT 317-318, *318*
CIVET 318-319
Civil engineering 566
Clairvoyance 588
CLASS 319
CLASSIFICATION OF LIVING
    ORGANISMS 319-320, *320*
Clastic rock 1457
Claude, Georges 835
CLAVICLE 321
CLAY 321-322, *321*
CLICK BEETLE 322
CLIMATE 322-325, *322*, *324*
Climatology 323
CLIMBING PLANT 325
CLINOMETER 325
Clock *1713*, *1714*
CLOCK AND WATCH 325-330,
    326, *327*, *329*
CLONE 330; 704
Closed circulatory system 316
CLOUD 331-332, *331*, *332*
Cloud chamber 10
CLOVE 332
CLOVER 332, *333*
CLUB MOSS 333, *333*
CLUTCH 333-334; 124
Clutch, fluid 333-334
CNIDARIA 334
COAL 334-337, *335*, *336*, 246; 559
COAL GAS 337, *337*
Coal mining 336-337
Coal, bituminous 336
COAST 337-338, *338*
Coastal deposition 338
Coastal erosion 338
COBALT 339

COBOL 365; 1062
COBRA 339, *339*
Cobweb 1595
COCA PLANT 339-340
Coccus 135
COCKATOO 340, *340*
COCKLE 340
COCKROACH 340-341, *340*
Cockroft, John 8
COCONUT 341-342, *341*
COD 342, *342*
COELACANTH 342, *342*
COENOCYTE 342, *342*
COFFEE 342-344, *343*
COHERENT LIGHT 344
COHESION 344
Coincidence range finder 1414
COKE 345
Cold front 665
Cold rolling 1464
Cold storage 646
Cold zone 323
COLD, COMMON 345-346
COLD-BLOODED ANIMAL 345, *345*
COLLAGEN 346
COLLENCHYMA 346, *346*
COLLOID 346-347, *346, 347*
COLOBUS 347-349, *348*
Colon 865
COLOR 349-350, *349, 350*
COLOR BLINDNESS 351, *351*
Color photography 1259-1262
Color printing 1349-1350
Color television 1688-1689
COLORADO POTATO BEETLE 350
COLORIMETRY 351-352
COMA 352; 3
COMA BERENICES 352
COMBUSTION 352
Combustion chamber 694
COMET 352-353, *353*; 1568-1569
COMMENSALISM 353-354; 1662
COMMUNICATION 354-358, *357*
Communication cable 221
Communication satellite 107; 1486-1487
COMMUTATOR 358
COMPASS PLANT 358-359
Complementary color 350
COMPOSITE FAMILY 360-361, *359*
COMPOUND 360
Compound microscope 1065-1066
Compound ore 1196
Compression chamber 695
Compression-type refrigerator 1427
Compressive stress 1633
COMPRESSOR 360-361; 694
COMPUTER 361-365, *361, 362, 363, 364*; 66; 121-122; 304, 305, 358; 410
Computer language 364-365
Computer memory 363
Computer programming 364-365
Concorde 34, *36*; 129
Concrete dam 416
CONDENSATION 365-366, *365*
CONDENSER 366, *366*
Conditioning 922
CONDOR 366-367, *367*
Conduction 770; 1426
CONDUCTION OF ELECTRICITY 367-368
CONDUCTION, HEAT 367, *367*
Conductive cable 221
Conductor 368; 770
Cone-bearing tree 1734
Cones (eye) 592
CONFORMITY 368

Congenital heart disease 767
CONGLOMERATE 368
CONIFER 368-370, *369*; 1734, 1735
CONNECTIVE TISSUE 370, *370*
CONSCIOUSNESS 370-371
CONSERVATION 371-372, *371, 372*
Conservation of energy 557
CONSTELLATION 372-373, *372*
Contact catalyst 257
Contact herbicide 781
Contact process 1647-1648
Contact system 1778
Container ship 1522
CONTINENTAL DRIFT 373, *373, 374*
Continental glacier 722
CONTINENTAL SHELF 374
Continuous filament fiber 606-607
CONTOUR 374, *374*
CONTRACEPTION 374
Contrail 113
CONVECTION 374-375, *375*; 770
Convectional lifting 1412
Converging lens 927
CONVEYOR 375-376
Conveyor belt 375-376
CONVULSION 376
Cooke, W. F. 518
Cooling system 562-563
COOLING TOWER 376-377
COORDINATES 377, *377*
COOT 377-378, *378*
COPERNICUS 378; 108, 109, *108*; 1757
COPPER 378-379, *379*
COPPER SULFATE 380
COPPERHEAD 379-380
CORAL 380, *380*; 115
Coral reef 380
CORAL SNAKE 381
CORIOLIS EFFECT 381
CORK 381-382, *381*
CORMORANT 382, *382*
CORN 382-383, *382*
Cornea 591
Corona 1649
Coronary disease 768
Coronary thrombosis 186
Corpuscular radiation 874
CORROSION 383-384, *383*
Corrosive poison 1308
CORTEX 384; 200
CORUNDUM 384
Cosine 1737
COSMIC RAYS 384
COSMOLOGY 385-386, *385*
COTTON 386-387, *386*
Cotton meal 386-387
COTTONMOUTH 387
Cottonseed oil 386
COTYLEDON 387-388
COULOMB 388
COULOMB, CHARLES DE 388; 518
COUSTEAU, JACQUES-YVES 388, *388*
COWBIRD 388-389
COWRIE 389
COYOTE 389, *389*
CPU 362, 364
CRAB 389-390, *390*
CRAB NEBULA 390; 1373
CRACKING 390; 692; 1248
CRANE 390-391, *391*
CRANE (BIRD) 392, *392*
CRANE FLY 392
Crankshaft 561-562
CRAPPIE 392
CRAYFISH 392

CREOSOTE BUSH 392-393
Crest 1809
Crested myna 1129
CRETACEOUS PERIOD 393, *393*
CRICK, FRANCIS HARRY COMPTON 393
CRICKET 393-394, *393*
CRINOID 394
CRITICAL TEMPERATURE 394; 690-691
CRO-MAGNON 395
CROCODILE 394-395, *394*
CROCUS 395
CROOKES, SIR WILLIAM 395-396
CROSSBILL 396, *397*
Crossing 216
Cross-pollination 1315
CROTON 396
CROW 396
CROWFOOT FAMILY 396
CRUSTACEAN 396, *398-399*
Crustose lichen 933
CRYOGENICS 399-401, *400*
CRYOLITE 401
Cryotron 400-401
CRYSTAL 401-403, *402*
Crystal system 402-403
CUCKOO 403, *403*
CUCUMBER 403
Culex 1110
Cumulative frequency graph 1616
Cumuliform cloud 332
Cuneiform 133; 1170-1171, *1170-1171*
CUPRONICKEL 404
CURIE 404
CURIE FAMILY 404-405
Curie, Marie 404-405
Curie, Pierre 404
Curing 647
CURIUM 405
CURLEW 405
CURRANT 405
Current 1181
CURRENT, ELECTRIC 405-407, *406*
CURVE 407-408, *407, 408*
Curved mirror 1082
CUTICLE 408
CUTTLEFISH 408, *408*
CUVIER, BARON 408-409, *409*
CYANIDE 409
CYBERNETICS 409-410, *410*
CYCAD 410-411
CYCLAMEN 411, *411*
CYCLE 411
Cyclic aliphatic hydrocarbon 818
CYCLONE 411-412, *412*
Cyclonic wind 811
CYCLOPS 412, *412*
CYGNUS 412
Cylinder block 561-562
Cylinder head 561-562
CYPRESS 412
Cyst 1366
Cytokinin 798
CYTOLOGY 413
CYTOPLASM 413

D

DAFFODIL 413
DAGUERRE, LOUIS 413
DAGUERREOTYPE 413-414; 233
Dairy cattle 260
DAISY 414, *414*
DALTON, JOHN 414-415, *414*; 1269

DAM 415-416, *415*
DAMPING 416
DANDELION 416, *417*
DARTER 416-417
DARWIN, CHARLES 418-419, *418*; 577-578, 580
DATE PALM 419, *419*
DATING 419-420, *419*
DAVY, SIR HUMPHRY 420, *420*
DAY 420, *421*
DC generator 701-702
DDT 851
DE FOREST, LEE 427
Dead reckoning 1133
Dead Sea Scrolls 91
DEATH 420, *422*
DEATHWATCH BEETLE 422
DECIBEL 422-423, *422*
DECIDUOUS TREE 423, *423*
DECOMPOSITION 423; 294
DEER 424-425, *424*
Deer mouse 1118
DEFENSE MECHANISM 425-427, *425, 426, 427*
DEGREE 427, *429*
DEGREE-DAY 429
DEHISCENCE 429
DELIQUESCENCE 429
DELPHINUS 429
DELTA 429, *428*
DELTOID 429-430
DEMOCRITUS 430
Denominator 659
DENSITY 430
Dental microbiologist 1057
DENTISTRY 430-431, *430*
Depressant 478-479
DEPRESSION 431-432, *432*
DESALINATION 432-434, *433*
DESCARTES, RENÉ 434-435, *434*
DESICCATOR 435, *435*
Destructive distillation 458
Detection 1239
DETERGENT 435-436
DEUTERIUM 436; 773
DEVONIAN PERIOD 436, *436*
DEW 437
DEW POINT 437; 30
DEWAR FLASK 437, *437*
DIABETES 437-438; 1270
Diabetes insipidus 438
Diabetes mellitus 437
Diamagnetism 990
DIAMOND 439-441, *439, 440*; 245
DIAPHRAGM 441
Diastolic pressure 186-187
DIATOM 441
DICOTYLEDON 442
DIE 442, *442*
Die casting 255
DIESEL 442-443, *442, 443*
Diesel engine 443
Diesel locomotive 957, 959
Diesel, Rudolf 443, *442*
DIET 443-446, *444, 445*
Dietetics 1172
DIFFERENTIAL 446-447; 124
DIFFERENTIATION, CELLULAR 447
DIFFRACTION 447-448
DIFFUSION 448
DIGESTION 448-449, *449*; 1441
Digital computer 361, 362
Digital watch 330
DIKE 449-450, *449*
DINGO 450
DINOSAUR 450-453, *450, 451, 452*
Diode 1763
DIOECIOUS 453
DIOPTER 453

Dipper dredge 473
DIRECT CURRENT 453, 405-407
DIRIGIBLE 453-454; 126
Discrimination 1239
DISEASE 454-456, *455, 456*
Diseases, dog 465
DISINFECTANT 456
Disk brake 202
Disk drive 1061
Dispersion by air 457
Dispersion by animals 457
Dispersion by explosion 457
Dispersion by water 457
DISPERSION OF LIGHT 456
DISPERSION OF PLANTS
    456-457, *457*
DISSOCIATION 457-458
DISTILLATION 458, 432
Distortion 3
DISTRIBUTOR 458-459
Diverging lens 927-928
DIVING 459-460, *459, 460*
Division 95
DNA 461; 172; 312; 330; 447;
    703-704; 937; 1092; 1164,
    1164-1165
DOCTOR 461-462
DODO 462
DOG 462-465, *462, 463, 464, 465*
DOGBANE FAMILY 465
DOGFISH 466, *466*
DOGWOOD 466
Doldrums 1825
DOLOMITE 466
DOLPHIN 466-467, *467*
DOMINANCE 467-468
DONKEY 468
DOPPLER EFFECT 468-469, *468*
DORMANCY 469
DORMOUSE 469, *469*
Double helix 461
Double replacement 294
Double star 1612
DOUGLAS FIR 469-470, *470*
DOVE AND PIGEON 470, *470*
Downy mildew 1072
Drag 24
DRAGONFLY 470-471, *471*
Drake, Edwin 1246
DREAM 472, *472*
Dredge 473
DREDGING 473; 1079
DRILLING 473-475, *474, 475*
Drilling machine 984
Drilling rig 474
Drive shaft 124
Drive train 124
Drone 160
Drop-hammer forging 653
DRUG 476-480, *477, 478, 480*
Drug abuse 479
Drug addiction 479
Drug therapy 1368
Drum brake 202
DRUMLIN 480
DRUPE 481, *481*
Dry cell battery 152-153
DRY CLEANING 481-482
Dry fruit 666
Drying (food) 646
DUCK 482-483, *482*
DUCKWEED 483
DUCTILITY 483
DUNE 483-484, *484*
DUNG BEETLE 485
Duodenum 865
DYE 485-487, *486*
DYNAMICS 487-488, *488*
DYNE 488
DYSENTERY 488-489

DYSPROSIUM 489

E

EAGLE 489-491, *490*
EAR 491-492, *492, 492-496, 493,
    495*; 109; 1288
Earth science 175
EARTHQUAKE 496-498, *496, 497,
    498*
EARTHWORM 498-499
EARWIG 499
Eastern hemisphere 777
Eastern hemlock 778
EASTMAN, GEORGE 499
EBONY 499-500
ECG 524
ECHIDNA 500, *500*
ECHINODERMATA 500-501, *500*
ECHO 501; 14-15
Echolocation 150-151
ECLIPSE 501-503, *501, 502*
ECLIPTIC 503
ECOLOGY 503-504; 175
ECOSYSTEM 504-506, *504-505,
    506, 507*; 1640
Ectoparasite 1219
ECZEMA 507
EDISON, THOMAS ALVA 507-508,
    517-518; 1112-1113; 1682
EEL 508, *509*
EFFERVESCENCE 509
EFFICIENCY 509-510
EFFLORESCENCE 510
Effort 981
Egg 850
EGGPLANT 510, *510*
EGRET 510-511
Egyptian calendar 228
EHRLICH, PAUL 511
EIDER 511
EINSTEIN, ALBERT 511-512, *511,*
    557; 1020; 1147; 1254; 1381,
    1429-1431; 1498; *1430*
EINSTEINIUM 512
EKG 524
ELAND 512-513, *512*
Elastic limit 1044
ELASTICITY 513-514, *513*; 1044
ELASTIN 514
ELDERBERRY 514
ELECTRIC BELL 514, *514*
Electric clock 329
Electric field 541; 614
ELECTRIC FISH 515, *515*
Electric furnace 678
Electric furnace process 1622
Electric heating 275-276
ELECTRIC LIGHT 521-522, *522*
Electric locomotive 959-960
ELECTRIC MOTOR 522-524, *522,
    523, 524*
Electric rocket 1459-1460
Electrical condenser 366
Electrical engineering 567
ELECTRICITY 515-518, *516, 517,*
    559
ELECTRICITY SUPPLY 518-521,
    519, 520-521
ELECTROCARDIOGRAM 524
ELECTROCHEMISTRY 524-525
ELECTRODE 525
Electrodialysis 432, 434
ELECTROENCEPHALOGRAPH
    526
ELECTROLYSIS 527-528, *527,
    528, 537-538*
Electrolyte 526, 527

Electromagnet 530, 531
ELECTROMAGNETIC
    RADIATION 528-529, *529*; 874
ELECTROMAGNETISM 529-531,
    530
ELECTROMOTIVE FORCE 531
ELECTROMOTIVE SERIES
    531-532
ELECTRON 532; 115; 1222, 1224
ELECTRON MICROSCOPE
    536-537, *536, 537*; 1068
ELECTRON VOLT 537
ELECTRONIC MUSIC 532-533,
    533; 1579-1580
Electronic navigation 1133-1134
ELECTRONICS
    533-536, *534, 535, 536*
ELECTROPHORESIS 537
ELECTROPLATING 537-538, *538*
ELECTROSCOPE 539, 541
ELECTROSTATICS 539-542, *540*
ELEMENT 542-546, *544-545*
Elementary particle 82
ELEPHANT 546-549, *547, 548*
ELEPHANT SEAL 549-550, *549*
ELEPHANT SHREW 550, *550*
ELK 550-551
Elliptical galaxy 681-682
ELM 551
EMBRYO 551-553, *552, 553*; 1433
Embryo, human 579-580
Embryophyte 1292
EMERALD 553-554, *554*
EMERY 554
Emigration 1071
EMOTION 554
EMULSION 554-555
ENAMEL 555
ENDOCRINE 555
Endocrine gland 723
Endoparasite 1219-1220
Endoskeleton 1537
ENDOSPERM 555
ENDOSPORE 555-556
ENDOTHERMIC REACTION 556
ENERGY 556-560, *556, 558, 559;*
    671
Energy conversion 557
ENGINE 560-564, *563*; 123-124
ENGINEERING 564-567, *565*
ENIAC 536
ENTOMOLOGY 567
ENTROPY 567
ENVIRONMENT 568, *568*, 504
ENZYME 568
EOCENE EPOCH 569
EPHEMERAL PLANT 569
EPIDEMIC 569, *569*
Epidermis 1541
EPILEPSY 569-570
EPIPHYTE 570
EPITHELIUM 570, *570*
EPSOM SALT 570
Equation (algebra) 44, 45
EQUATOR 571; *1342*
Equilateral triangle 712
EQUILIBRIUM 571
EQUINOX 571
EQUIVALENT 571
ERBIUM 571
ERG 571-572
Ergot 675
Erie Canal 240
Eros (asteroid) 103-104
EROSION 572, *572*
Eruption (volcanic) 1789
Erythrocytes 186
ESCALATOR 573
ESOPHAGUS 572
ESP 588

ESTER 573-574, *573*
ETHANE 574, *574*
ETHER 574
ETHYLENE 574, *574*
EUCALYPTUS 574-575, *575*
Euclid 1018
EUROPIUM 575-576
Eutrophication 1640
EVAPORATION 576
EVENING PRIMROSE FAMILY
    576, *576*
EVERGREEN 577, *577*
EVOLUTION 577-580, *578, 579*
EXCAVATION 580-581, *580*
EXCRETION 581-582, *581*
EXOBIOLOGY 582-583, *582, 583*
Exocrine gland 723
Exoskeleton 100; 848, 850; 1537
Exosphere 114
EXOTHERMIC REACTION 584;
    770
Expandable balloon 141, 142
Expandable clay 321
EXPANSION 584
Expiration 1443
Exploding star 1612
EXPLOSIVE 584-586, *585*
EXPONENT 586-587
Exponents, laws of 586-587
Exposure 1256-1257
EXPOSURE METER 587; 1257
Exterior ballistics 139
External communication 354-355
External respiration 1441-1442
EXTRASENSORY PERCEPTION
    587-588
EXTRUSION 589, *589*; 1301
Extrusive rock 834
EYE AND VISION 589-594, *590,
    591, 593*
Eye, defects of 592-593
Eye, diseases of 593-594

F

Factory robot 1455
Fahrenheit 271
FAHRENHEIT SCALE 594
FAIRY SHRIMP 594, *594*
FALCON 594-596, *595*
Fallopian tube 1433
FALLOUT 596, *596*
FALSE SCORPION 596-597
FAMILY 597
FARAD 597
FARADAY CONSTANT 598
FARADAY, MICHAEL 597, *597*; 72;
    517
Fast-breeder reactor 1162-1163
FAT 598, *598*; 444; 1173
FATHOM 598
FAULT 598-599, *599*
Faulting 1116
FEATHER 599-600, *600*
FEATHER STAR 600
FEEDBACK 600-601, *600*
FELDSPAR 601-602, *601*
FEMUR 602
FERMENTATION 602-603, *602*
FERMI, ENRICO 603
FERMIUM 603
FERN 603-605, *603, 604*; 1252
Ferric compound 872
Ferromagnetism 990
Ferrous compound 872
FERTILIZATION 605, *605*; 1432,
    1433
FERTILIZER 605-606; 29

FEVER 606
FIBER 606-610, *607, 608, 609, 610*
FIBER OPTICS 612-613, *612, 613*
FIBERGLASS 610-611, *611*
Fibrous membrane 1032
Fibrous root system 1465
FIBULA 613
FIELD 613-614, *614*
Field curvature 3
Field effect transistor 1731-1732
FIG 614, *614*
FILBERT 615, *615*
FILM 1261, 1256
Film developing 1257, 1259
Film printing 1259
FILTER 615-616, *615, 616*
FILTER FEEDING 616
FINCH 616-617, *616*
Fine-wooled sheep 1519-1520
Fingerprint 652
FIR 617, *617*
FIRE 617-618
Fire extinguisher 620
FIRE PROTECTION 618-622, *619, 620, 621*
Firebrat 209-210
FIREFLY 618, *618*
First generation robot 1456
First law of thermodynamics 1701
FISH 622-625, *622, 623, 624, 624-625, 625*
FISSION 625-626, *626*; 117
FITCH, JOHN 626-627
Fixed-focus camera 235
FJORD 627
Flaccid paralysis 1218
FLAGELLATE 627, *627*; 1364
FLAGELLUM 627-628
Flake soap 1557
FLAMINGO 628, *628*
Flatbed press 1348-1349
FLATFISH 628-629, *628*
FLEA 629, *629*
FLEMING, SIR ALEXANDER 629, *629*; 77; 1236
FLICKER 630
FLINT 630, *630*
FLOREY, HOWARD WALTER 630, *630*; 1236
FLOWER 630-633, *631, 632, 633*; 1294
Flowering tree 1734, 1735
FLOWMETER 633
FLUID 633
Fluid cat cracking 390
Fluid dynamics 634
FLUID MECHANICS 634-635, *634*
FLUIDICS 633-634
FLUORESCENCE 635, *635*
FLUORIDATION 635-636
FLUORIDE 636, *636*
FLUORINE 636
FLUX 636-637
FLY 637, *637*
FLYING FISH 637-638, *638*
FLYING FOX 638, *638*
FLYWHEEL 638-639, *638*
FM 1394
Focal length 928
FOCUS 639-640, *639*
FOG 640, *640*
FOLDING 640-641, *640*; 1116
Foliose lichen 933
FOOD 641-643, *642*
FOOD CHAIN 643-644, *643*
Food groups 446; 1173-1174, *1172-1173*
FOOD POISONING 644
FOOD PRESERVATION 644-648, *645, 646, 647*

FOOT-POUND 648
FOOT-POUND-SECOND SYSTEM 648-649, *648*
FOOTCANDLE 648
FORAMINIFERIDA 649, *649*
FORCE 649
Forced-air furnace 676-677
FORD, HENRY 650-651, *650*; 122
Forensic ballistics 139
FORENSIC SCIENCE 651-652, *651*
FORESTRY 652, *652*
FORGING 652-653, *653*
FORMALDEHYDE 653, *653*; 41
FORSYTHIA 654
FORTRAN 365; 1062
FOSSIL 654-657, *654, 655, 656, 657, 579*
FOUCAULT PENDULUM 657-658, *657*
FOUCAULT, JEAN 657
Fourdrinier machine 1215
FOX 658, *658*
FOXGLOVE 658-659, *658*
FRACTION 659
Fractional distillation 458
FRACTURE 659-660, *659*
FRANCIUM 660
FRANKLIN, BENJAMIN 660, *660*
Fraunhofer, Joseph 109
Freeze-drying 647
Freezing 432, 434
Freezing (food) 646
FREEZING AND FREEZING POINT 660-661, *661*
FREEZING MIXTURE 661
Freighter 1522
FREON 661
FREQUENCY 661-662, *662*; 1576-1577; 1810-1811
Frequency modulation 1394
Freshwater environment 504
FREUD, SIGMUND 662-663, *662*; 21; 1368, 1370
FRICTION 663-664, *663*
Friction clutch 333
FRIGATE BIRD 664, *664*
FROG 664-665, *665*
FRONT 665
Frontal lifting 1412
FROST 666
Fructose 1642
FRUIT 666-667, *667*
FRUIT FLY 668
Fruticose lichen 933
FUCHSIA 668
FUEL 668-671, *668, 669, 670*
FUEL CELL 671
FULLER'S EARTH 671
FULMAR 672
FULTON, ROBERT 672
Functional disorder 1035
FUNGICIDE 672
FUNGUS 673-676, *673, 674, 675*
Fungus kingdom 319
FURNACE 676-678, *676, 677*
FUSE, ELECTRIC 678-679, *679*
FUSION 679, *680*; 117
Fusion, nuclear 679-680

G

Gabor, Dennis 794-795
GADOLINIUM 680
GAGARIN, YURI ALEKSEYEVICH 680-681, *680*
GALAXY 681-684, *681, 682, 683, 684*

GALEN 684
GALENA 685; 917
GALILEO 685-686, *685*; 108; 1267
GALL WASP 686-687, *686*
GALLBLADDER 686
Galle, J. G. 109
GALLIUM 686
GALVANI, LUIGI 687, *687*; 517
GALVANIZING 687-688, *688*
GALVANOMETER 688-689, *688*
GAMETE 689
GAMMA RAY 689
GANNET 689
GAR 689
GARLIC 689
GARNET 690, *690*
GARTER SNAKE 690
GAS 690-691, *691*; 542; 1021
Gas balloon 141, 142
Gas chromatography 311
GAS METER 691-692
Gas refrigerator 1427-1428
GAS TURBINE 694-696, *694, 695*; 1746, 1748
Gaseous fuel 670
GASOLINE 692-693, *692*
Gasoline engine 249; 560-564; 692-693
GASTROCNEMIUS 693
GASTROPOD 693-694, *693*
GAUSS 696
GAUSS, KARL FRIEDRICH 696-697; 1018
GAVIAL 697
GAY-LUSSAC, JOSEPH 697, *697*
GAZELLE 697-698, *697*
GEAR 698-699, *698*
GECKO 699, *699*
GEIGER COUNTER 699-700
GEMINI 700
GENE 700; 312; 467; 578; 702-703
General circulation 1825, 1826
General dentistry 431
GENERATOR, ELECTRICAL 700-702, *701, 702*
Genetic engineering 704
Genetic screening 704-705
GENETICS 703-705, *704*; 782
GENUS 705
Geochemical prospecting 1360-1361
GEOCHEMISTRY 705-706
GEODESY 706
GEOGRAPHY 706-707
GEOLOGICAL MAP 707, *707*
Geological oceanography 1180
Geological time 1714
GEOLOGICAL TIME SCALE 707-709, *708*
GEOLOGY 709-711, *710*
GEOMETRY 711-714, *711, 712, 713, 714*
GEOMORPHOLOGY 714
Geophysical prospecting 1360
GEOPHYSICS 714-715
Geostational satellite 1487
Geostationary satellite 1053
GEOSYNCLINE 715
Geothermal energy 559-560
Geotropism 1118
GERANIUM 715
GERBIL 715
GERM 715-716
GERMANIUM 716
GERMINATION 716-717, *716*; 1509
Gestalt psychology 1370
GESTATION PERIOD 717
GEYSER, SPRING AND 1603
Ghorkhar 103
Giant panda 1213
GIANT SEQUOIA 717

GIANT STAR 717-718; 1612
GIBBERELLINS 718; 798
GIBBON 718, *718*
GILA MONSTER 719
GILBERT, WILLIAM 719; 1267
GILLS 719
GINGER FAMILY 719-720
GINKGO 720
GINSENG FAMILY 720
GIRAFFE 720-721, *720*
GLACIATION 721, *721*
GLACIER AND ICE SHEET 722, *722*
GLADIOLUS 722
GLAND 722-723, *723*
GLASS 723-727, *725, 726*
Glass blowing 725-727
GLAUBER'S SALT 727
GLAUCOMA 727
GLENN, JOHN HERSCHEL 727-728, *727*
Globulin 477
Glomar Challenger 1182
Glomerulus 894
GLUCOSE 728, *728*; 245; 1642
GLUTEUS MAXIMUS 728
GNEISS 728
GNETALES 728-729
GNU 729
GOAT 729, *729*
GODDARD, ROBERT HUTCHINGS 729-730, *730*
GOLD 730-732, *730, 731*
Gold-leaf electroscope 539
GOLDENROD 732, *732*
GOLDFISH 732
GONADS 732-733
GONORRHEA 733
Goodyear, Charles 1468
GOOGOL 733
Googolplex 733
GOOSE 733-734
GOOSEBERRY 734
GOOSEFOOT FAMILY 734
GOPHER 734
GORILLA 734-735, *735*
GOSHAWK 735
GOURD FAMILY 735-736
GOVERNOR 736, *736*
Grab dredge 473
GRACKLE 736
Graf Zeppelin 454
Graham's law *691*
GRAIN WEEVIL 736-737
GRAND CANYON 737, *737*
GRANITE 737-738, *737*
Granulated soap 1558
GRAPE 738, *738*
GRAPEFRUIT 738-739
GRAPH 739-740, *739, 740*
Graphic instrument 854
GRAPHITE 740
GRASS 741, *741*
GRASSHOPPER 742-743, *742, 743*
Grasshopper mouse 1118
Gravel culture 826
Gravitational field 614
GRAVITY 743-744, *744*; 24
Gravity meter 1079
Gravure printing 1348
Gray squirrel 1607
GRAY, ASA 744
Grazing grass 741
Great auk 119
GREAT BARRIER REEF 744, *744*
GREAT CIRCLE 745
Great gray kangaroo 889
Great Pyramid 1378
Great Wall of China 303
GREBE 745

Green tea 1674
Greenhouse effect 325
GREENWICH MEAN TIME 745
Greenwich meridian 1342
Gregorian calendar 228
GRINDING AND POLISHING 745-
747, *745*, *746*
Grissom, Virgil 1354
GRIZZLY BEAR 747, *747*
GROSBEAK 747
GROUNDHOG 747-748
GROUNDING 748
GROUNDWATER 748-749, *748*
GROUPER 749
GROUSE 749
GROWTH 749-750, *750*
GRUNION 750-751
GUANACO 751, *751*
GUANO 751
GUERICKE, OTTO VON 751
Guided missile 1083
GUINEA PIG 751-752
Gulf Stream 1180
GULL 752, *752*
GUN 752-754, *753*, *754*
Gunpowder 586
GUPPY 754
Gutenberg, Johann 356-357; 1346
GUTTA-PERCHA 754
GYMNOSPERM 754-755, *754*, *755*;
1252, 1293
GYPSUM 755
GYROSCOPE 755-756, *755*

H

HABER, FRITZ 756
Habitat 505
HACKBERRY 756
HADDOCK 756-757
HAFNIUM 757
HAGFISH 757, *757*
HAHNIUM 757
HAIL 757-758
HAIR 758
Hair hygrometer 829
Hair seal 1502
HALF LIFE 758-759, *759*
Halftone 1347
HALIBUT 759
HALLEY'S COMET 759-760, *759*;
353
HALLUCINATION 760
Hallucinogen 478
HALOGEN 760
Halogen family 868
HALOPHYTE 760, *760*
Hammerhead crane 391
HAMMERHEAD SHARK 760
HAMSTER 761
HAMSTRING 761
Hanging Gardens 133
Hardening 773
HARDNESS 761-762, *761*
Hardwood lumber 971
HARE 762
HARMONICS 762
HARRIER 762-763, *763*
HARTEBEEST 763
Harvest mouse 1118
HARVESTMAN 763, *763*
HARVEY, WILLIAM 763-764
HAUSTORIA 764
HAWK 764
HAWKMOTH 764, *764*
HAWTHORN 765
H-bomb 1163-1164
HbS 1527

Head 847-848
HEARING AID 765-766, *765*
HEART 766-767, *766*
HEART DISEASE 767-768
Heart transplant 768
HEARTWOOD 769
HEAT 769-771, *770*
HEAT SHIELD 771-772, *771*, *772*
HEAT TREATMENT 772-773
HEATH FAMILY 771, *771*
HEAVY ELEMENT 773
HEAVY WATER 773
HEISENBERG, WERNER 773
HELICOPTER 773-775, *774*, *775*
HELIOGRAPHY 775
HELIUM 775-776, *776*; 1155
HELLBENDER 776
HELMHOLTZ, HERMANN 777
Helmont, Jan Baptista van 297
HEMATITE 777, *777*
HEMISPHERE 777
HEMLOCK 777-778
HEMLOCK TREE 778
HEMOCYANIN 778
HEMOGLOBIN 778; 66-67
Hemoglobin-A 778
Hemoglobin-S 778
HEMOPHILIA 778-779
HEMORRHAGE 779
HEMP 779
HENNA 779-780
HENRY 780
Henry Draper Catalogue 110
HENRY, JOSEPH 780
HERB 780
HERBACEOUS PLANT 780-781,
780, *781*
HERBICIDE 781-782, *781*
HERBIVORE 782
HERCULES 782
Hereditary disease 784
HEREDITY 782-784, *783*; 312; 703
HERMAPHRODITE 784-785
HERMIT CRAB 785, *785*; 390
HERNIA 785
HERON 785-786, *786*
HERPES 786; 300
HERPETOLOGY 786
HERRING 786-787
HERSCHEL, SIR JOHN
        FREDERICK WILLIAM 787
Herschel, Sir William 109; 1760
HERTZ 787
HERTZ, HEINRICH 787; 356; 518;
942; 1811
Heterozygous plant 783
HIBERNATION 787-788, *788*
HIBISCUS 788-789, *788*
HICKORY 789
Hieroglyphics 355; 1171, *1171*
HI-FI 789-790
High explosive 584, 586
High pressure system 1813
High tide 1711-1712
High-alloy steel 1620
Himalayan black bear 183
Hindenburg 454
HIPPARCHUS 791
HIPPOCRATES 791
HIPPOPOTAMUS 791-792, *791*
HISTOLOGY 792
Historical geology 710
HIVES 792-793
Hoff, Marcian E., Jr. 535-536
HOFMANN, AUGUST 793
HOFSTADTER, ROBERT 793
HOLLY FAMILY 793, *793*
HOLLYHOCK 793-794
HOLMIUM 794
Hologram 794, 795, 796

HOLOGRAPHY 794-796, *794*, *795*
Home furnace 676-677
HOMEOSTASIS 796
Homeothermic animal 1797
Homo erectus 808
Homo sapiens 808
HOMOLOGUE 796-797, *796*
Homozygous plant 782
Honey 157
HONEY LOCUST 797
Honeybee 158-159
HONEYSUCKLE FAMILY 797, *797*
Hooke joint 1756, *1756*
HOOKE, ROBERT 797-798, *798*
HOP 798
HORIZON 798
HORMONE 798-801
HORNBEAM 801
HORNBILL 801
HORNBLENDE 801
HORNET 801-802
HORSE 802-803, *802*
HORSE CHESTNUT 803
HORSEFLY 803-804, *803*
HORSEHEAD NEBULA 804
HORSEPOWER 804
HORSERADISH 804
HORSETAIL 804-805, *804*, *805*
HORTICULTURE 805
Hot rolling 1464
Hot spring 1603
Hot-air balloon 142
Hourglass 328
House mouse 1117-1118
House myna 1129
HOUSEFLY 805-806, *805*
HOWLER MONKEY 806, *806*
HOYLE, SIR FRED 806
HUBBLE, EDWIN POWELL 806-
807; 1424
Hue 350
HUMAN BEING 807-809
Human eye 591
Human geography 705
HUMBOLDT, BARON
        ALEXANDER VON 809
HUMERUS 809
HUMIDITY 809; 30
HUMMINGBIRD 809-810, *810*
HUMUS 810, *810*; 1560, 1561
Hunting spider 1594-1595
HURRICANE 810-811, *812*
HUTTON, JAMES 812, *812*
HUYGENS, CHRISTIAN 812; 941;
1810
HUYGENS' PRINCIPLE 812;
1809-1810
HYACINTH 812
HYATT, JOHN WESLEY 812-813
HYBRID 813; 383; 783
HYDRA 813-814, *814*
HYDRANGEA 814
HYDRATE 814-815
Hydraulic dredge 473
Hydraulic engine 816
Hydraulic machines 816-817
Hydraulic press 817
HYDRAULICS 815-817, *815*, *816*
HYDRAZINE 817
HYDRIDE 817
HYDROCARBONS 817-818
HYDROCHLORIC ACID 819
Hydrodynamics 634
Hydroelectric plant 821
HYDROELECTRIC POWER 819-
821, *820*
HYDROFOIL 821-822, *821*
HYDROGEN 822-823, *822*, *823*
Hydrogen bomb 1163
HYDROGEN BOND 823-824, *824*

HYDROGEN PEROXIDE 824
HYDROGEN SULFIDE 824-825
Hydrokinetics 816, 817
HYDROLOGY 825, *825*
HYDROLYSIS 825, *825*
HYDROMETER 825-826, *826*
HYDROPONICS 826
Hydrosphere 494
HYDROSTATICS 826-828, *827*, 816
Hydrostatics, first law of 827
Hydrostatics, second law of 827
Hydrostatics, third law of 827-828
Hydrotropism 1118
HYDROXIDE 828, *828*
HYENA 828
HYGIENE 828-829, *829*
HYGROMETER 829
Hypertension 768
HYPHA 829; 673
HYPNOSIS 829-830
Hypodermic needle 847
Hypothalamus 202
HYSTERESIS 830, *830*

I

IBIS 830-831, *831*
ICBM 1083
ICE 831; 1802
ICE AGE 831-832, *831*
ICEBERG 832
ICELAND SPAR 832
ICHNEUMON FLY 832-833, *833*
ICHTHYOLOGY 833
ICHTHYOSAUR 833
ICONOSCOPE 833-834, *833*
IDEAL MECHANICAL
        ADVANTAGE 834
Idler gear 699
IGNEOUS ROCK 834, *834*; 1456-
1457
Ignition 562
IGUANA 834-835, *835*
ILLUMINATION 835
Illusion of movement 1190
Illusion of shape 1190
Image orthicon 834
IMAGINARY NUMBER 835
Immigration 1071
IMMISCIBLE LIQUID 835-836
Immovable joint 883
IMMUNITY 836-837, *836*
IMPACT 837
IMPALA 837-838, *838*
IMPEDANCE 838
IMPLANTATION 838-839
IMPLOSION 839
INCAN CIVILIZATION 839
INCANDESCENCE 839
INCENSE CEDAR 840
Inclined plane 981, 983
Incoherent light 344
Independent assortment, law of 703
INDIAN CIVILIZATION 840
INDICATOR 840, *841*; 1719
INDIGO 841
INDIUM 841
INDUCTION 842, *842*
INDUCTION (LOGICAL) 842
Induction furnace 678
Industrial diamond 441
Industrial furnace 677-678
Industrial microbiologist 1058
Industrial Revolution 1675
Inert pigment 1208
INERTIA 842-843
INERTIAL GUIDANCE 843
INFECTION 843

INFINITY 843
INFLAMMATION 845
INFLORESCENCE 845, *844*, *845*
INFLUENZA 845-846
INFRARED RAY 846, *846*
INFRASONICS 846
INGOT 846
Inheritance 784
Initial velocity 139
INJECTION 846-847, *847*
Injection molding 1301
Inner planet 1286
INORGANIC CHEMISTRY 847; 297
Inorganic compound 1196-1198
INSECT 847-851, *848*, *849*
INSECTICIDE 851, *851*, 850-851
INSECTIVORE 851-852, *852*
Insectivorous plants 252
Insight learning 922-923
INSOLATION 852
Inspiration 1443
Instant camera 236-237
Instant coffee 343
INSTINCT 852-853, *852*
Instinctive behavior 162
INSTRUMENT, SCIENTIFIC 853-854, *853*
Instrumental learning 922
INSULATION 854-855, *855*
Insulator 368; 770
INSULIN 855-857, *856*; 437-438
INTEGRATED CIRCUIT 857-859, *858*; 362; 535; 1062; 1677
INTELLIGENCE 859-861, *860*
INTENSITY 861; 1577
Interactive television 358
INTERFERENCE 861-862, *862*; 941-942; 1192
INTERFEROMETER 862
INTERFERON 862; 1784-1785
Interior ballistics 139
INTERNAL COMBUSTION ENGINE 862-863, *863*
Internal communication 354
Internal respiration 1442
INTERNATIONAL DATE LINE 864, *864*
INTERNATIONAL SYSTEM 864
Interphase 1088
INTESTINE 865
Intrusive rock 834
INVENTION 865-867, *866*
INVERSE SQUARE LAW 867
INVERTEBRATE 867-868, *868*; 70
IODIDE 868
IODINE 868-869, *869*
Ion 116
Ion rocket 1460
Ionic compound 870, 871
Ionosphere 113-114
IONS AND IONIZATION 869-871, *870*
IQ 171
IRIDIUM 871
Iris (eye) 591-592
IRIS FAMILY 871, *871*, *872*
IRON 872-874, *873*
IRON AGE 874
IRRADIATION 874
Irrational number 1170
IRRIGATION 874-875, *875*
Irritant poison 1308
ISOBAR AND ISOTHERM 875
ISOMER 875-876, *876*
Isosceles triangle 712
ISOSTASY 876-877
Isostatic balance 877
ISOTOPE 877-878; 116, *117*

J

JACARANDA 878
JACKAL 878, *878*
Jacquard, Joseph Marie 120; 1675
JADE 878
JAGUAR 879, *879*
JAMES, WILLIAM 879
Janssen, Pierre 776
JASMINE 879
JASPER 879
JAVA MAN 879-880
Jefferson, Thomas 90
JELLYFISH 880, *880*
JENNER, EDWARD 880-881; *1762*
Jet engine 35; 881
JET PROPULSION 881, *881*
JET STREAM 881-882, *882*
JODRELL BANK 882
JOINT (ANATOMY) 882-884, *883*
JOINT (GEOLOGY) 884
Joliot-Curie, Irène 405
JOULE 884
JOULE EFFECT 884-885
JOULE, JAMES PRESCOTT 884
JOULE-THOMSON EFFECT 885
Julian calendar 228
JUNCO 885
JUNG, CARL GUSTAV 885
JUNGLE CAT 885-886
JUNIPER 886, *886*
JUPITER 886-887, *886*; 107, 109; 1288
JURASSIC PERIOD 887, *887*
JUTE 887-888

K

KALEIDOSCOPE 888, *888*
KANGAROO 888-889
KANGAROO RAT 889
KAOLIN 889-890, *890*; 322
Kaon 1224
KARST SCENERY 890, *890*
KEKULE VON STRADONITZ, FRIEDRICH 890-891, *891*
Kelvin 1056
KELVIN, LORD 891, *891*
KELVIN SCALE 891; 5
KEPLER, JOHANN 891-892, *892*; 108, 109; 200
Keplerian telescope 1685-1686
KERATIN 892
KEROSENE 892
KESTREL 892, *892*
KETONE 893
Kiang 103
KIDNEY 893-894, *893*
KILN 894
Kilogram 1055
KINETIC ENERGY 894-895; 488, 557
KINETIC THEORY 895
KING CRAB 895
KINGDOM 895-896
KINGFISHER 896, *896*
KINKAJOU 896, *896*
KIRCHHOFF, GUSTAV ROBERT 897
KIRCHHOFF'S LAWS 897
KITE 897
KIWI 897, *898*
KOALA 897-898, *897*
KOCH, ROBERT 898-899, *899*
KODIAK BEAR 899
KOLA NUT 899

KOMODO DRAGON 899, *899*
KOOKABURRA 899-900, *900*
KREBS CYCLE 900; 1442
KRILL 900
KRYPTON 900-901; 1155
KUDU 901, *901*
Kulan 103
KURCHATOVIUM 901

L

LABURNUM 901
LACEWING 901-902, *902*
LACQUER 902, *902*
LACTIC ACID 902-903
Ladder dredge 473
Ladder truck 621
LADYBUG 903, *903*
LAKES AND PONDS 903-904, *904*
LAMARCK, JEAN BAPTISTE 904-905
Lamp, arc 522
Lamp, fluorescent 522
LAMPREY 905, *905*
LANCELET 905-906
Land pollution 1318
Land snail 1551
LANDSLIDE 906
LANTHANUM 906
LAPIS LAZULI 906, *906*
LARCH 907, *907*
Large intestine 865
LARK 907
LARVA 907-908, *908*; 850
LARYNX 908, *908*
LASER 908-911, *909*, *910*; 344; 794, 795-796
LATENT HEAT 911-912
Lateral bud 212-213
Latex 1468
Latex paint 1208
LATHE 912-913, *912*; 984
LATITUDE AND LONGITUDE 913
LATTICE 913, 870
Laughing gas 1154
LAUREL 913
LAVA 913-915, *914*; 149; 1787
LAVENDER 915
LAVOISIER, ANTOINE 915, *915*; 297
LAWRENCE, ERNEST 915-916; 8
LAWRENCIUM 916
LAXATIVE 916
LCD (LIQUID CRYSTAL DISPLAY) 916-917
LEACHING 917
LEAD 917-918, *918*
Lead dioxide 918
Lead glass 724
LEAF 918-921, *920*; 1294
LEAF INSECT 921, *921*
LEAKEY, LOUIS S. B. 921-922; 77
LEAKEY, RICHARD E. 922
Learned behavior 162-163
LEARNING AND MEMORY 922-924, *923*, *924*
LED (LIGHT-EMITTING DIODE) 924, 612
LEECH 924-925, *925*
LEEK 925
LEEUWENHOEK, ANTON VAN 925, *925*
LEGUME 925
Leith, Emmett 794-795
LEMMING 925-926, *926*
LEMUR 926, *926*
LENS 926-928, *927*; 3
LENTIL 928-929

LENZ' LAW 929
LEO 929
LEONOV, ALEKSEY ARKHIPOVICH 929
LEOPARD 929-930, *929*
LEPROSY 930
Lepton 1224
LESSEPS, FERDINAND DE 930-931, *930*
Lesser panda 1213
Letterpress printing 1346-1347
LETTUCE 931
Leucocytes 186
LEUKEMIA 931; 241
LEVEE 931-932
Lever 981, 982-983
LEYDEN JAR 932
LIBBY, WILLARD FRANK 932
LIBRA 932
LICE 932-933, *933*
LICHEN 933-934, *934*
LICORICE 934
LIE DETECTOR 934-935
LIFE 935-939, *935*, *936*, *938*
Life cycle 938-939
Lift 23-24
LIGAMENT 939
LIGHT 939-943, *940*, *942*
LIGHT, COHERENT 344
LIGHTHOUSE 943-944, *943*
LIGHTNING 944, *944*; 515
LIGHT-YEAR 944
LIGNIN 945
LIGNITE 945; 336
LILAC 945
LILY FAMILY 945, *945*
LILY OF THE VALLEY 946
LIMESTONE 946, *946*
LIMPET 946-947, *947*
LINDEN 947
LINEAR INDUCTION MOTOR 947-948, *948*
LINNAEUS, CAROLUS 948
Linters 387
LION 948-949, *949*
LIQUEFACTION 949-950
LIQUID 950; 542; 1021
LIQUID AIR 950-951, *951*
Liquid fuel 670
Liquid propellant rocket 1459
Liquid-in-glass thermometer 1702
LISTER, JOSEPH 951
LITHARGE 951-952, 918
LITHIUM 952
Lithosphere 494
LITMUS 952; 840-841
LIVER 952-953
Liverwort 1110-1111
LIZARD 953
LLAMA 953-954, *954*
Load 981
LOAM 954
Lobe, frontal 200
Lobe, occipital 200
Lobe, parietal 200
Lobe, temporal 200
LOBELIA 1199
LOBSTER 954-955, *955*
Local wind 1826
LOCK 955-956, *956*
LOCK (NAVIGATIONAL) 956, *956*, *957*
Lockyer, Sir Joseph 775
LOCOMOTIVE 958-961, *958*, *959*, *960*, 962; 1408
LOCOWEED 962, *962*
LOCUST (tree) 963, *963*
LOCUST 963-964, *963*, *964*; 742-743
LODESTONE 964-965

LOESS 965
LOGARITHM 965-966
LOGARITHM TABLES 967-970
LOGO 365
Long-horned grasshopper 742
Long-wooled sheep 1519
LOON 971
Loose-fill insulation 855
LOOSESTRIFE FAMILY 971
Loudness 1577-1579
LOUDSPEAKER 971-972
LOVEBIRD 972
Lovell, James 1354
Low explosive 584, 586
Low pressure system 1813
Low tide 1712
Low-alloy steel 1620
LOWELL, PERCIVAL 972; 109; 1306
Lowland gorilla 735
Lubrication system 563
LUGWORM 972-973, *972*
LUMBER 973-974, *973*
LUMEN 974-975
LUMINESCENCE 975
Luminosity 1612
LUNG 975-976, *976*; 1443
Lung cancer 241
LUNGFISH 976-977, *977*
LUPINE 977, *977*
LUTETIUM 977-978
LYE 978
LYELL, SIR CHARLES 978
LYMPH 978
LYMPHATIC SYSTEM 978-979, *978*
Lymphocyte 836
Lymphoma 241
LYNX 979, *979*
Lyophilic colloid 347
Lyophobic colloid 347
LYRA 979-980
LYREBIRD 980, *980*

M

MACAW 980
MACH 981
MACHINE TOOL 983-986, *984, 985*
MACHINE, SIMPLE 981-983, *982*
MACKEREL 986, *986*
Macronutrient 605-606
Magic number 1169
MAGMA 986; 1076; 1786
MAGNESIUM 986-987, *987*
Magnet 989-990
Magnetic field 613-614
MAGNETIC POLE 987-988, *988*
Magnetic solenoid lock 955
MAGNETIC STORM 988
MAGNETISM 988-990, *989, 990*
MAGNETITE 990
MAGNETO 991
MAGNETOMETER 991; 1079
MAGNIFICATION 991-992, *991*
MAGNITUDE 992, *992*
MAGNOLIA FAMILY 992, *992*
MAGPIE 993
Maiman, Theodore 909
MALACHITE 993, *993*
MALARIA 993
MALLEABILITY 993-994
MALLOW FAMILY 994, *994*
MAMBA 994, *994*
MAMMAL 994-997, *995, 996, 997*
Mammary gland 1073
MAMMOTH 997, *997*
MANATEE 997-998

MANDRILL 998, *998*
MANGANESE 998-999
MANGO 999
MANGROVE 999, *999*
MANOMETER 999-1000, *1000*
MANTIS 1000-1001, *1000*
MANTLE 1001
MAP AND MAPPING 1001-1005, *1002, 1003, 1004*
MAPLE FAMILY 1005
MARBLE 1005-1006, *1005*
MARCONI, GUGLIELMO 1006-1007, *1006*; 1396-1397
MARIJUANA 1007
MARINE BIOLOGY 1007-1008
Marine chronometer 313
Marine environment 504-505
Marine propeller 1357
Marine snail 1552
MARL 1008
MARMOSET 1008, *1008*
MARMOT 1008-1009, *1008*
MARROW 1009
MARS 1009-1011, *1010*; 107, 109; 1288
MARSH GAS 1011
MARSUPIAL 1011-1013, *1012-1013*
MARTEN 1012-1013
MARTIN 1013
MASER 1013-1014; 911
MASS 1014
MASS ACTION, LAW OF 1014
Mass communication 356-358
Mass number 118
MASS PRODUCTION 1014-1015, *1015*
MASS SPECTROGRAPH 1015-1016, *1016*
Mass unit 118
MASTODON 1016
MATCH 1017-1018
MATHEMATICS 1017-1019, *1018*
MATRIX 1019-1020, *1019*
MATTER 1020-1021
Mature river 1451
Maximum and minimum thermometer 1702-1703
MAXWELL, JAMES CLERK 1021, *1021*; 518; 942
MAYAN CIVILIZATION 1021-1022
MAYFLY 1022, *1022*
Mead, Margaret 77
MEADOWLARK 1022-1023
MEASLES 1023
MEASUREMENT 1023-1024
Measuring instrument 854
Mechanical clock 328-329
MECHANICAL DRAWING 1024, *1024*
Mechanical engineering 566
Mechanical explosive 584
Mechanical refrigeration 1427
MECHANICS 1024-1025
MEDICAL ENGINEERING 1025-1026, *1025*
MEDICINE 1026-1028, *1027, 1028*; 297
Medium-sized star 1612
Medium-wooled sheep 1520
MEIOSIS 1029, *1029*; 266
Melanin 1277
MELON 1029-1030
MELTING POINT 1031, *1031*
MEMBRANE 1030-1032, *1031*
MENDEL, GREGOR 1032, *1032*; 28; 196; 782
Mendel's first law 782-783
Mendel's laws 702-703
Mendel's second law 783-784

MENDELEEV, DMITRI 1032-1033, *1033*; 298; 545-546
MENDELEVIUM 1033
MENISCUS 1033
MENSTRUAL CYCLE 1033-1034
MENSURATION 1034, *1034*
MENTAL HEALTH 1034-1036
Mental illness 1035
MENTHOL 1036
MERCURY (ELEMENT) 1037-1038, *1037*
MERCURY (PLANET) 1036-1037; 109; 1286, 1288
Mercury barometer 148
MERGANSER 1038
MERISTEM 1038, *1038*; 1717
MESA 1039, *1039*
MESON 1039; 8; 1224
MESOZOIC ERA 1039-1040, *1039*
METABOLISM 1040
Metal 542
METAL AND METALLURGY 1040-1046, *1041, 1042-1043, 1044, 1045*
METAL FATIGUE 1046
Metallurgical engineering 566-567
METALWORK 1046-1047, *1046*
METAMORPHIC ROCK 1047; 1457
METAMORPHOSIS 1047-1048, *1048*; 850
Metaphase 1088
METAZOA 1048; 807
METCHNIKOFF, ÉLIE 1048, *1048*
METEOR 1048-1049, *1049*
Meteor shower 1049
Meteorite 110; 1048, 1049
Meteoroid 1048, 1049; 1569
Meteorological satellite 1487-1488
METEOROLOGY 1050-52, *1051*
Meter 1054
METER-KILOGRAM-SECOND SYSTEM 1052
METHANE 1053
METRIC SYSTEM 1053-1054, *1054*
METRONOME 1055, *1055*
Metsat 1487-1488
MEYER, ADOLF 1055
MEYER, JULIUS L. 1055
MICA 1055-1056, *1056*
MICHELSON, ALBERT ABRAHAM 1056
Microbiologist 1057
MICROBIOLOGY 1057-1058, *1058*
Microchip 305
MICROCOMPUTER 1058-1062, *1059, 1060, 1061*
MICROELECTRONICS 1062
MICROFILM 1062-1063
MICROMETER 1063, *1063*
MICRON 1063
MICROORGANISM 1064, *1064*
MICROPHONE 1064-1065, *1065*
Microprocessor 305; 1058
MICROSCOPE 1065-1068, *1066, 1067*
MICROTOME 1068, *1068*
MICROWAVE 1068, *1068*
MIDNIGHT SUN 1069, *1069*
MIGRATION 1069-1071, *1070, 1071*
MILDEW 1071-1072
MILK 1072-1073, *1072*
MILKY WAY 1073-1074, *1073*; 682-684
Milled soap 1557-1558
MILLET 1074
MILLIBAR 1074
MILLIKAN, ROBERT ANDREWS 1074
Milling machine 984

MILLIPEDE 1074, *1074*
MIMICRY 1075-1076, *1075*
MIMOSA 1076
MINERAL 1076-1077; 444; 1173
Mineral tanning 1666
MINERALOGY 1077
MINING 1077-1080, *1078, 1079*
Mining engineering 566
MINK 1080
MINNOW 1080-1081
MINT FAMILY 1081, *1081*
MIOCENE EPOCH 1081
MIRAGE 1081
MIRROR 1081-1083, *1082*
MISSILE 1083-1085, *1084, 1085*
Missile submarine 1638
MISSISSIPPIAN PERIOD 1085, *1085*
MIST 1085
MISTLETOE 1085-1086, *1086*
MITE 1086, *1086*
MITOCHONDRIA 1086-1087
MITOSIS 1087-1088, *1087*; 266
MIXTURE 1088
Mobile crane 391
MOCK ORANGE 1088-1089
MOCKINGBIRD 1088
Modem 1061
MODERATOR 1089
MODULATION 1089
MOHO 1089
Mohs scale 761-762; 1077
Moisture 1815
MOLD 1089-1090
MOLE 1090; 131
MOLE (UNIT) 1090
MOLECULAR BIOLOGY 1090-1092, *1091*
MOLECULAR WEIGHT 1092-1093
MOLECULE 1093
MOLLUSCA 1093-1095, *1093, 1094*
MOLTING 1095
MOLYBDENITE 1095
MOLYBDENUM 1095
MOMENT 1095-1096, *1096*
MOMENTUM 1096
MONEL METAL 1096
MONERA 1096
Monera kingdom 319
Mongoloid 808
MONGOOSE 1096-1097
MONITOR LIZARD 1097
MONKEY 1097-1099, *1097, 1098*
MONKEY PUZZLE 1099
MONOCARPIC PLANT 1099
MONOCOTYLEDON 1099-1100, *1100*
MONOECIOUS 1100
MONONUCLEOSIS 1100
MONORAIL 1100-1101, *1101*
MONOTREME 1101-1102, *1101*
MONSOON 1102, *1102*
Montgolfier, Etienne 141
Montgolfier, Joseph 141
MOON 1102-1106, *1103, 1104*; 107; 1353, 1354
Moon rock 1105
MOOSE 1106, *1106*; 424
MORAINE 1106, *1107*; 721
MORGAN, THOMAS HUNT 1107; 784
MORNING GLORY 1107
MORPHOLOGY 1107
MORSE CODE 1108, *1108*
MORSE, SAMUEL FINLEY BREESE 1107-1108; 355-356; · 518; 1680
MORTAR 1108-1109
MOSQUITO 1109-1110, *1109*; 455

MOSS AND LIVERWORT 1110-1111, *1110, 1111*
MOSS ANIMAL 1111-1112
MOTH, SILKWORM 1529
MOTION PICTURE 1112-1115, *1113, 1114, 1115*
Motion, first law of 487
Motion, second law of 487
Motion, third law of 487
Motion-picture camera 237
Motor nerve 1143
MOTORCYCLE 1115-1116, *1116*
MOUNTAIN 1116-1117, *1117*
MOUNTAIN ASH 1117
Mountain gorilla 735
MOUSE 1117-1118
MOVEMENT OF PLANTS 1118-1119, *1119*
MUCOUS MEMBRANE 1119, *1119*; 1032
MUD PUPPY 1119
MULBERRY 1120
MULE 1120, *1120*
MULLET 1120
MULTIPLE SCLEROSIS 1120-1121
Multiple-response learning 922
Multiplication 94
Multistage rocket 1459
MUMPS 1121
Muon 1224
MUSCLE 1121-1124, *1122, 1123*
MUSHROOM 1124-1125, *1125*
MUSK OX 1125-1126, *1126*
MUSKELLUNGE 1125
MUSKRAT 1126
MUSSEL 1126-1127, *1127*
MUSTARD FAMILY 1127-1128, *1128*
MUTATION 1128, *1128*; 579; 784
Mute swan 1659
Mutualism 1662
Mycelium 673-674
MYNA 1129
MYRTLE FAMILY 1129

N

NAIL 1129-1130, *1129*
NAPHTHALENE 1130
NAPIER, JOHN 1130
NARCISSUS 1130
NARCOTIC 1130
NARWHAL 1131
NASA 1131, *1131*
Nasal passage 1157-1158
Nastic movement 1119
NASTURTIUM 1131-1132
NATIONAL PARK 1132
Native metal 1196
Natural fiber 607-608
Natural resin 1437
NATURAL RESOURCE 1132
Natural rubber 1468, 1470
Natural satellite 1485
Natural selection 578, 579
NAUTILOID 1132-1133
NAVIGATION 1133-1135, *1134, 1135, 1136*
Navigation satellite 107; 1488
NEANDERTHAL 1136; 808
Neap tide 1712
Neat soap 1557
NEBULA 1136, *1136, 1137*
NECTARINE 1138
NEGATIVE NUMBER 1138
Negroid 808
NEKTON 1138-1139, *1138*
NEMATODE 1139
NEODYMIUM 1139

NEON 1139-1140, *1139*; 1155
Neoplasm 456
NEOPRENE 1140
NEOTENY 1140, *1140*
NEPTUNE 1141, *1141*; 109; 1288
NEPTUNIUM 1141
Nernst heat theorem 1702
NERVE CELL 1141-1142, *1142*
Nerve impulse 1142
NERVOUS SYSTEM 1143-1144, *1143*
NETTLE FAMILY 1144, *1144*
Network (radio) 1396
Neuron 1141-1142, 1143, 1144
Neurosis 1035
NEUTRAL STATE 1144-1145
NEUTRALIZATION 1144
NEUTRINO 1145; 8; 1224
NEUTRON 1145-1146; 115; 1169; 1222, 1224
NEUTRON STAR 1146
New World monkey 1099
New World porcupine 1325
Newcomen, Thomas 1618-1619
NEWT 1146, *1146*
NEWTON 1146
NEWTON'S RINGS 1147-1148, *1148*
NEWTON, SIR ISAAC 1146-1147, *1147*; 108-109; 743; 941; 1267; 1686
NICKEL 1148-1149, *1149*
NICKEL SILVER 1149
NICTATING MEMBRANE 1149
NIGHTHAWK 1149, *1149*
NIGHTSHADE FAMILY 1150, *1150*
NIOBIUM 1150
NITRATE 1150-1151, *1151*
NITRIC ACID 1152
Nitride 1152
NITROGEN 1152
NITROGEN CYCLE 1153, *1153*
NITROGEN FIXATION 1154, *1153, 1154*
NITROUS OXIDE 1154
NOBEL PRIZE WINNERS IN SCIENCE 1155
NOBEL, ALFRED 1154-1155
NOBELIUM 1155
NOBLE GAS 1155
NOBLE METAL 1155
NOCTURNAL HABIT 1156, *1156*
NODE 1156-1157, *1157*
Nonexpandable clay 321-322
Non-metal 542
Non-selective herbicide 781
NORMAL SOLUTION 1157
NORTH STAR 1157, *1157*; 168
Northern hemisphere 777
NOSE 1157-1158, *1158*
NOTOCHORD 1158, *1158*
NOVA 1158-1159, *1159*
NPN transistor 1731
Nuclear energy 559
Nuclear explosive 586
Nuclear fission 282-283; 1160-1161, 1162
NUCLEAR PHYSICS 1159-1160
NUCLEAR POWER 1160-1163, *1161, 1162*
Nuclear reactor 1161-1163
Nuclear rocket 1460
NUCLEAR WEAPONS 1163-1164, *1168*
NUCLEIC ACID 1164, *1164-1165*
Nucleon 1145
Nucleotide 461
Nucleus 115
NUCLEUS, ATOMIC 1164-1169, *1166, 1167, 1168*

NUMBER 1169-1170, *1170*
NUMERAL 1170-1171, *1170, 1171*
Numerator 659
Nutation 1118-1119
NUTHATCH 1172
NUTRITION 1172-1174, *1172-1173*
NYLON 1174
NYMPH 1175, *1175*

O

OAK 1175, *1175*
OAK RIDGE NATIONAL LABORATORY 1175-1176
OATS 1176
OBSERVATORY 1176-1179, *1177, 1178, 1179*
OBSIDIAN 1179-1180
Ocean bed 1181
Ocean current 1180-1181, *1180*
Ocean wave 1181
Oceanographic research ship 1522
OCEANOGRAPHY 1180-1183, *1180, 1182, 1183*
OCELOT 1183
OCTANE RATING 1183-1184
OCTOPUS 1184, *1184*
Offset lithography 1347-1348
Offset printing 1347-1348
OHM 1185
OHM'S LAW 1185
OHM, GEORG SIMON 1185; 518
OIL SHALE 1185
Oil-base paint 1208
Old river 1451
Old World monkey 1099
Old World porcupine 1325
OLEFIN 1185-1186
Oleoresinous varnish 1769
OLIGOCENE EPOCH 1186
OLIVE FAMILY 1186
OLM 1186, *1186*
OMNIVORE 1186
Onager 103
ONION 1187
ONYX 1187
OOGONIUM 1187
OOZE 1187
OPAL 1187-1188, *1188*
OPAQUE PROJECTOR 1188
Open circulatory system 316
Open hearth process 1622
Open pit mining 1079
Open tower 377
Ophthalmology 594
OPOSSUM 1188-1189, *1189*
Optic nerve 592
Optical condenser 366
Optical fiber 612
OPTICAL ILLUSION 1189-1191, *1189, 1190*
Optical isomer 876
Optical pyrometer 1379
Optical recording 1420-1421
Optical system 1779
Optical telescope 1176-1178, *1177*
OPTICS 1191-1192, *1192*
ORANGE 1192-1193
ORANGUTAN 1193-1194, *1193*
ORBIT 1194, *1194*
ORCHID FAMILY 1194-1195, *1195*
ORDER 1195-1196
ORDOVICIAN PERIOD 1196
ORE 1196
ORGAN 1196
ORGANELLE 1196
ORGANIC CHEMISTRY 1196-1198, *1197*; 297

Organic compound 1196-1198
Organic fertilizer 606
Organic mental illness 1035
ORGANISM 1198
ORIOLE 1198
ORION 1198
Ornamental grass 741
Ornithischia 451-453
ORNITHOLOGY 1198-1199
Orographic lifting 1412
Orthodox sleep 1544
OSCILLATION 1199, *1199*
OSCILLATOR 1199
OSCILLOSCOPE 1200, *1200*
OSMIUM 1200
OSMOSIS 1200-1201, *1201*
OSPREY 1201-1202, *1201*
Osteoporosis 194
OSTRICH 1202, *1202*
OTTER 1202
Outer planet 1286
OVARY 1202-1203
OVENBIRD 1203
OWL 1203, *1203*
OXALIC ACID 1203
OXIDATION AND REDUCTION 1203-1204
Oxidation number 1204
OXIDE 1204
OXYACETYLENE TORCH 1204-1205, *1205*
OXYGEN 1205-1206, *1205*
Oxygen cycle *1205*
OYSTER 1206, *1206*
OZONE 1207

P

PABA 1644
Pacemaker 768
PACK RAT 1207
PADDLEFISH 1207
Padlock 955
PAGODA TREE 1207
PAIN 1207-1208
PAINT 1208-1209, *1209*
PALEOBOTANY 1210
PALEOCENE EPOCH 1210
PALEOCLIMATOLOGY 1210
PALEONTOLOGY 1210–1211
PALEOZOIC ERA 1211-1212, *1211*
PALLADIUM 1212
PALM FAMILY 1212, *1212*
Panama Canal 239
PANCREAS 1212; 856, 857
PANDA 1212-1213, *1213*
PANGOLIN 1213-1214, *1214*
PANSIES, VIOLETS AND 1782, *1783*
PANTOGRAPH 1214
PAPER 1214-1216, *1215*
Paper chromatography 309-311
Paper recycling 1216
Papyrus 1214
PARACHUTE 1216-1217, *1216*
Paradoxical sleep 1544
PARAFFIN 1217
PARAKEET 1218
PARALLAX 1218
Parallel circuit 315
PARALYSIS 1218
PARAMECIUM 1218-1219, *1219*
PARASITE 1219-1220, *1220*
Parasitism 1662
Parathyroid gland 799-800
PARENCHYMA 1220-1221
PARROT 1221, *1221*
PARSEC 1221

PARSLEY FAMILY 1221
PARSNIP 1221
PARTHENOCARP 1221
PARTHENOGENESIS 1221-1222; 101
Partially movable joint 883
Particle accelerator 1159, 1223
PARTICLE PHYSICS 1222-1224, *1223*
Pascal's theorem 827
PASCAL, BLAISE 1224-1225, *1225*; 827
PASCAL'S TRIANGLE 1225, *1225*
Passenger ship 1522
PASSIONFLOWER 1225-1227, *1226*
Passionfruit 1227
Passive immunity 837
PASTEUR, LOUIS 1227, *1227*
PASTEURIZATION 1227
PATELLA 1227
PATHOLOGY 1227-1228; 175
PAULI, WOLFGANG 1228
PAULING, LINUS 1228, *1228*
PAVLOV, IVAN PETROVICH 1228, *1228*
PEA FAMILY 1229-1230
PEACH 1229, *1229*
PEAFOWL 1230
PEANUT 1230, *1230*
Peanut oil 1230
PEAR 1231
PEARL 1231-1232, *1231*
PEAT 1232, *1232*; 336
PECCARY 1232-1233
PECTIN 1233
PECTORALIS MAJOR 1233
Pedocal soil 1561
PEGASUS 1233
PEKING MAN 1233
PELICAN 1233-1234, *1234*
PELVIS 1234-1235
PENDULUM 1235-1236, *1235*; 1532
PENGUIN 1236, *1237*
PENICILLIN 1237-1238, *1236*
PENNSYLVANIAN PERIOD 1238
Penstock 820-821
PEONY 1238
PEPPER FAMILY 1238-1239
PERCENTAGE 1239
PERCEPTION 1239
PERCH 1239-1240
PERCHING BIRD 1240
Percussion instrument 1579
PERENNIAL PLANT 1240
PERIANTH 1240
PERIODIC MOTION 1240
Periodic table 545-546, *544-545*
Periodontics 431
PERISCOPE 1240-1241, *1241*
PERISTALSIS 1241
Permanent-mold casting 255
PERMIAN PERIOD 1241, *1241*
PERPETUAL MOTION 1242, *1242*
PERSEUS 1242
Personal communication 355
Personal computer 305; 1060
PERSPECTIVE 1242, *1243*
PESTICIDE 1243-1244, *1243, 1244*
PETAL 1244
Petiole 919
PETREL 1244, *1244*
PETRIFIED FOREST 1244
PETROLEUM 1245-1248, *1245, 1246, 1247, 1248*; 390
PETROLOGY 1249
PEWEE 1249, *1249*
PEWTER 1249
PH 1250; 12; 149; 840, 841

PHALANGES 1250
PHARMACOLOGY 1250, *1250*; 172
PHASE 1250-1251
PHEASANT 1250-1251
PHENOLS 1251
PHEROMONE 1251; 1673
PHLEBITIS 1251
PHLOEM 1251-1252, *1252*
Phlogiston 297
Phlox 1252, *1252*
PHOEBE 1252-1253
Phonograph 356; 1421-1422
PHOSPHATE 1253
PHOSPHORESCENCE 1253, *1253*
PHOSPHORIC ACID 1254
PHOSPHORUS 1254
Photoconductivity 1255
PHOTOELECTRIC EFFECT 1254-1256, *1255*; 942
Photoemission 1254
Photoengraving 1346
PHOTOGRAPHY 1256-1262, *1256, 1257, 1258, 1259, 1260, 1261*
Photoionization 1254
Photometer 587; 1262
PHOTOMETRY 1262-1263, *1262*
PHOTON 1263
Photonasty 1119
PHOTOPERIODISM 1263
Photosphere 1649
PHOTOSYNTHESIS 1263-1264, *1263, 1264, 1292*
Phototypesetting 1348
Photovoltaic effect 1255
Phyla (animal) 69
PHYLUM 1265
PHYSICAL CHANGE 1265
PHYSICAL CHEMISTRY 1265; 297-298
Physical geography 705
Physical geology 708-710
Physical oceanography 1180
Physical property 1021
PHYSICS 1265-1266
PHYSICS, HISTORY OF 1266-1270, *1266, 1267, 1268*
PHYSIOLOGY 1270; 175
PHYSIOTHERAPY 1270-1271, *1271*
Pi 1170
PIAGET, JEAN 1271-1272
PICCARD, AUGUSTE 1272, *1272*; 151-152
PICKEREL 1273
Pickup cartridge 790; 1422
Picture graph 1616
Pie chart 1616
Piezoelectric crystal 403
PIEZOELECTRIC EFFECT 1273-1274, *1273*
PIG 1274-1276, *1275, 1276*
PIG IRON 1276, *1276*; 872
Pigeon 470
PIGMENT 1276
PIGMENTATION 1277
PIKA 1277
PIKE 1277
PILING 1277-1278
PILOT FISH 1278, *1278*
Piloting 1133
PILTDOWN MAN 1278
Pin-tumbler cylinder lock 955, 956
PINE FAMILY 1279, *1279*
Pine marten 1013
PINEAL GLAND 1278
PINEAPPLE 1278-1279, *1279*
Pinion 698
PINK FAMILY 1280, *1280*
Pion 1223, 1224
PIPEFISH 1280

PIPETTE 1280-1281, *1280*
PIRANHA 1281, *1282*
PISCES 1281
PISTIL 1281
Piston compressor 360
PIT VIPER 1283-1284
PITCH 1281
PITCHBLENDE 1281
PITOT TUBE 1281, 1283, *1283*
Pitot, Henri 1283
Pituitary gland 723; 799
Place value 1171
PLACENTA 1284, *1284*
Placer mining 1079
Plain bearing 154-155
Plain position indicator 1389
PLANCK, MAX 1284; 1381
PLANCK'S CONSTANT 1285
PLANE FAMILY 1285, *1285*
Plane geometry 711
Plane mirror 1082
PLANET 1285-1289, *1287, 1288*; 1568
PLANETARIUM 1289, *1289*
PLANKTON 1289-1290, *1290*
Plant breeding 205-206
PLANT DISEASE 1290-1291, *1291*
PLANT KINGDOM 1291-1296, *1293, 1295*; 319
Plant tissue 1717-1718
PLANTAIN FAMILY 1290
Plants, study of 196
PLASMA 1296; 186
PLASMA (PHYSICS) 1297
PLASMODIUM 1297; 1547, 1548
PLASTER OF PARIS 1297
PLASTIC 1297-1302, *1298, 1299, 1300, 1301*
PLASTIC SURGERY 1302
PLATE TECTONICS 1302-1303, *1302*; 711; 1788-1789
Platelets 1297
PLATINUM 1303, *1303*
PLATYHELMINTHES 1303
PLATYPUS 1303-1304
PLEISTOCENE EPOCH 1304, *1304*
Pleistocene ice age 831-832
PLIMSOLL LINE 1304
PLIOCENE EPOCH 1305
PLOVER 1305
PLUM 1305, *1305*
PLUTO 1306, *1306*; 109; 1289
PLUTONIUM 1306-1307
Plutonium-239 1162
Pneumatic caisson 223
PNEUMATICS 1307
PNEUMATOPHORE 1307
PNEUMONIA 1307-1308
PNP transistor 1731
POD 1308
POISON 1308
Poison ivy 1310
POISONOUS PLANT 1308-1310, *1309*
POLAR BEAR 1310-1311, *1310*
Polar satellite 1053
Polaris 1157
POLARIZED LIGHT 1311
POLAROID CAMERA 1311-1312, *1312*
POLE 1312-1313
POLECAT 1313
Polio 1313
POLIOMYELITIS 1313
Political geography 705-706
POLLEN 1313-1314, *1314*
POLLINATION 1315-1316
POLLUTION 1316-1318, *1317, 1318*

Pollution control 1318
POLONIUM 1319
Polycarbonate disk 791
POLYESTER 1319
POLYETHYLENE 1320-1321, *1320, 1321*
POLYGON AND POLYHEDRON 1320-1321, *1320, 1321*
Polygraph 934
Polymer 1300
POLYMERIZATION 1321-1322, *1322*; 1300
POLYMORPHISM 1322, *1322*
POLYP 1322
Polypeptide 800
POLYSTYRENE 1322-1323
POLYURETHANE 1323
POME 1323
POMEGRANATE 1323, *1323*
PONDWEED 1323-1324, *1323*
POPLAR 1324, *1324*
POPPY FAMILY 1324, *1324*
PORBEAGLE 1324-1325
PORCUPINE 1325, *1325*
PORPOISE 1325, *1325*
PORTLAND CEMENT 1326
PORTUGUESE MAN-OF-WAR *1326*
Potash alum 53-54
POTASSIUM 1326-1327
POTATO 1327
POTENTIAL 1327-1328
Potential energy 557
POTHOLE 1328, *1328*
Pottery 278
POULTRY 1328-1329, *1329*
POUNDAL 1329-1330
POWDER METALLURGY 1330
Powdery mildew 1072
Powell, Cecil 1223
POWER 1330
PPI 1389
PRAIRIE DOG 1330-1331, *1330*
PRASEODYMIUM 1331
PRAWN 1331, *1332*
PRECAMBRIAN ROCK 1331
PRECAMBRIAN TIME 1331, 1333, *1333*
PRECESSION 1333-1334, *1334*
PRECIOUS STONE AND GEM 1334-1336, *1335*
PRECIPITATE 1336-1337
PRECIPITATION 1337
Precognition 588
Prefabrication 214
PREGNANCY 1337-1338
PREHISTORY 1338
Press forging 653
PRESSURE 1338-1339, *1339*
PRESSURE GAUGE 1340, *1340*
Pressure microphone 1064
Prevailing wind 1825
PRIESTLEY, JOSEPH 1340, *1340*; 541; 1152; 1205
Primary colors (light) 349
PRIMATE 1340-1342, *1341*; 807
PRIME MERIDIAN 1342, *1342*
Prime pigment 1208
PRIMROSE FAMILY 1342-1343, *1343*
PRINTED CIRCUIT 1343-1344, *1344*
Printer 1061
PRINTING 1345-1350, *1345, 1347, 1349*; 356-357
Printing press 1348-1349
PRISM 1350
PROBABILITY 1350-1351, *1351*
PROBOSCIS MONKEY 1351-1352, *1351*
PROBOSCIS WORM 1352

PROCAINE 1352
PROCYON 1352
PRODUCER GAS 1352-1353
Programming language 1061-1062
PROJECT APOLLO 1353-1355, *1353, 1354, 1355*
Projection (map) 1005
PROJECTOR 1355-1356, *1355*
PROMETHIUM 1356
Prominence 1649-1650, *1650*
PRONGHORN 1356, *1356*
PROPANE 1356-1357
PROPELLER 1357-1358, *1357*
Prophase 1088
PROPRIOCEPTION 1358
Proprioceptor 1358
Prosimian 1342
PROSPECTING 1358-1361, *1359, 1360*; 1078
PROSTAGLANDIN 1361
PROSTHETICS 1361
PROTACTINIUM 1361
PROTECTIVE COLORATION 1362
PROTEIN 1362, *1362*; 57; 444; 1173
Protein synthesis 1164
PROTEROZOIC ERA 1362-1363
PROTISTA 1363; 673
Protista kingdom 319
PROTON 1363; 115; 1145; 1169, 1222, 1223, 1224
PROTOPLASM 1363
PROTOZOA 1363-1366, *1364-1365, 1366*
PROXIMA CENTAURI 1366; 1612
PRUSSIC ACID 1366-1367
PSILOPHYTE 1367, *1367*
PSYCHIATRY 1367-1368
PSYCHOANALYSIS 1368; 1036; 1370
Psychokinesis 588
PSYCHOLOGY 1369-1371
Psychosis 1035
PSYCHOSOMATIC DISORDER 1371
Psychotherapy 1036; 1367-1368
Psychrometer 829
PTERIDOPHYTE 1371-1372, *1371*
PTERODACTYL 1372, *1372*
PTOLEMY 1372-1373; 92; 108; 1756
PUFF ADDER 1373, *1373*
PUFFIN 1373, *1373*
Pulley 981, 983
PULSAR 1373
PULSE 1374
Pulse radar 1388
PUMA 1374, *1374*
PUMICE 1374, *1376*
PUMP 1376, *1375*
Pumper 621
PUPA 1376-1377, *1377*; 850
Pupil reflex 1425-1426
Pure mathematics 1017
Pure science 1498
PURSLANE FAMILY 1377
PVC 1377-1378
PYRAMID 1378, *1378*
PYRITE 1378
PYROMETER 1378-1379
Pythagoras 108
PYTHAGOREAN THEOREM 1379, *1379*
PYTHON 1379-1380, *1380*

Q

QUADRANT 1380, *1380*
QUAIL 1380-1381

QUANTA 1381
QUANTUM THEORY 1381-1382
QUARK 1382-1383
QUARRYING 1383, *1383*; 1080
QUARTZ 1383-1385, *1384*
QUARTZITE 1385
QUASAR 1385; 111; 1612
QUATERNARY PERIOD 1385
Queen bee 159-160
QUICKSAND 1385
QUININE 1385-1386, *1386*

R

RABBIT 1386-1387, *1387*
RABIES 1387
RACCOON 1387-1388, *1388*
Rack and pinion gear 699
RADAR 1388-1391, *1389, 1390*; 533; 1134
Radiant heating 275
RADIATION 1391, *1391*; 770; 874; 1399-1400
Radiation pyrometer 1378-1379
RADICAL 1391-1392
RADIO 1392-1397, *1393, 1394, 1395*; 357-358
RADIO ASTRONOMY 1400, *1400*
RADIO CONTROL 1400-1401, *1401*
Radio station 1392, 1396
RADIO TELESCOPE 1404-1405; 1178-1179; 1686; *1179*
Radio wave 1394, 1396
Radioactive isotope 877
RADIOACTIVE SERIES 1397
RADIOACTIVITY 1397-1400, *1398, 1399*; 404-405
Radiocarbon dating 419-420
RADIOGRAPHY 1401-1402
RADIOISOTOPE 1402
RADIOLARIAN 1403, *1403*
RADIOLOGY 1403, *1403, 1404*
RADIOSONDE 1403, *1404*; 1050-1051, 1053
RADIOTHERAPY 1405
RADISH 1405-1406
RADIUM 1406
RADIUS 1406
RADON 1406; 1155
Radula 694
RAILROAD 1407-1411, *1407, 1408, 1409, 1410*
Railway track 1408
RAIN 1411-1413, *1412*
RAIN GAUGE 1413
RAINBOW 1413, *1413*
RAINMAKING 1413-1414
RAISIN 1414
RAM 363; 1060
RAMSAY, SIR WILLIAM 1414; 776
Random Access Memory 1060
RANGE FINDER 1414-1415, *1415*
Range height indicator 1391
RAOULT'S LAW 1415
RARE EARTH ELEMENT 1415
RASPBERRY 1415-1416
RAT 1416, *1416*
Rational number 1170
RATTLESNAKE 1416-1417, *1417*
RAVEN 1417
RAY 1417
Rayleigh scattering 1494
Rayleigh, Baron 1493
RAYON 1417-1418, *1418*
REACTANCE 1418-1419
REACTION, PRINCIPLE OF 1419
Read Only Memory 363, 1060

Recall 923
RECENT EPOCH 1419
RECEPTACLE 1419
Reception 1426
RECEPTOR 1419
Reciprocating pump 1376
Recognition 923; 1239
RECORD PLAYER 1421-1422, *1421*
RECORDING, SOUND 1419-1421, *1420*
Rectangular number 95
RECTIFIER 1422-1423, *1423*
RECYCLING 1423
Red kangaroo 889
RED SHIFT 1423-1424
Red squirrel 1607
REDBUD 1423
REDWOOD 1424, *1424*
REED 1424-1425
REED, WALTER 1425
Reference map 1001
Reflecting telescope 1176-1177; 1686
REFLECTION OF LIGHT 1425, *1425*
Reflective insulation 855
REFLEX 1425-1426, *1426*
Refracting telescope 1176; 1684-1685
Refraction 941; 1191-1192
REFRACTION OF LIGHT 1426-1427
REFRIGERATOR 1427-1428
REGENERATION 1428; 101
REINDEER 1428-1429, *1429*
RELATIVE DENSITY 1429
Relative humidity 809
RELATIVITY 1429-1431, *1430*
Relativity, theory of 511-512
Relearning 923
REM 1431
REM (Rapid Eye Movements) 472
REMORA 1431, *1431*
REMOTE CONTROL 1431
Replacement 294
REPRODUCTION 1431-1435, *1434*
REPRODUCTIVE SYSTEM 1435
REPTILE 1436-1437, *1436-1437, 1438*
Rescue truck 621
RESIN 1437-1438, *1438*
Resistance furnace 678
Resistance thermometer 1704
RESISTANCE, ELECTRICAL 1438-1439
RESISTOR 1439
RESONANCE 1439-1440, *1440*; 15-16
RESPIRATION 1441-1442, *1441*
RESPIRATORY SYSTEM 1442-1444, *1443*
Response 1426
Reverberation 15
Reynolds, Osbourne 634
Rh system 187
RHENIUM 1444
RHEUMATIC FEVER 1444; 767-768
RHI 1391
RHINOCEROS 1444-1445, *1445*
RHIZOME 1445-1446
RHODIUM 1446
RHODODENDRON 1446-1447, *1446*
RHUBARB 1447
RIB 1447
RIBOSOME 1447
RICE 1447-1448, *1448*
Richardson, Lewis Fry 1051-1053

RICHTER SCALE 1448
Rickets 194
RICKETTSIA 1448-1449
RIFT VALLEY 1449
Right triangle 712
RIGHT WHALE 1449
Rigid insulation 855
RINGHALS 1449, *1449*
Rings of Saturn 1489
RINGWORM 1449-1450
RIVER 1450-1452, *1450, 1451, 1452*
RNA 1452-1453; 172; 1031; 1164, *1164-1165*
ROADRUNNER 1453, *1453*
Robber crab 785-786
ROBIN 1453
Robot 986; 1453, 1456
ROBOTICS 1453-1456, *1454, 1455*
ROCK 1456-1457
Rock drill 474
ROCK SALT 1461
ROCKET 1457-1461, *1458, 1460*; 881; 1083
Rocket engine 1457
Rocket fuel 1458
RODENT 1461-1463, *1462*
Rods (eye) 592
ROEMER, OLAUS 1463
ROENTGEN 1463
ROENTGEN, WILHELM CONRAD 1463
Roller bearing 154
ROLLING 1463-1464, *1464*
ROM 363; 1060
Roman calendar 228
Roman numeral 93, 1171
ROOT 1464-1466, *1465*
ROOT CROP 1466
ROOT, MATHEMATICAL 1466
RORQUAL 1466-1467, *1466*
Rosary pea 1310
ROSE FAMILY 1467, *1467*
Rosetta Stone 91
ROSEWOOD 1467
Rotary compressor 360
Rotary press 1349
Rotary pump 1376
ROTIFER 1468
Rotor 523
Roundworm 101
RUBBER 1468-1471, *1469, 1470*
RUBBER TREE 1471
RUBIDIUM 1471
RUBY 1471-1472, *1472*
RUE FAMILY 1472
RUMINANT 1472; 74
RUSH 1472-1473, *1472*
RUST 1473
RUST AND SMUT 1473-1474, *1473, 1474*
RUTHENIUM 1474
Rutherford scattering 1494
Rutherford, Daniel 1152
RUTHERFORD, ERNEST 1474-1475, *1474*; 8; 1164, 1167, 1169, 1222; 1363; 1494; 1732
RUTHERFORDIUM 1475
RUTILE 1475
RYE 1475

S

Sabin vaccine 1476
SABIN, ALBERT BRUCE 1475-1476; 1313
SABLE 1476
Safety match 1017

SAGITTARIUS 1476
SALAMANDER 1476-1477, *1476*
SALINITY 1477
SALIVA 1477
Salk vaccine 1477
SALK, JONAS EDWARD 1477; 1313
SALMON 1477-1478, *1478*
SALTPETER 1478-1479
SALTS 1479
SAMARIUM 1479
SAN ANDREAS FAULT 1479-1480, *1479*
SAND 1480, *1480*
SAND AND SHOT BLASTING 1481
Sand casting 255
SAND DOLLAR 1481, *1481*
SANDALWOOD 1480-1481
SANDSTONE 1481-1482, *1482*
SAP 1482
SAPPHIRE 1482-1483
SAPROPHYTE 1483, *1483*
SAPSUCKER 1484, *1484*
Sarcodina 1364
SARDINE 1484
SARGASSO 1484
SASSAFRAS 1484
SATELLITE 1484-1488, *1485, 1486, 1487*
Saturation 350
SATURN 1488-1489, *1489*; 109; 1288
Saurischia 451
Savory, Thomas 1618
SAWFISH 1490, *1490*
SAWFLY 1490
Sawmill 974
SAXIFRAGE FAMILY 1490
SCALE 1490-1491
Scale (map) 1001-1002
SCALE INSECT 1491
SCALLOP 1491
SCANDIUM 1491
SCARAB 1492
SCARLET FEVER 1492
SCARP 1492
Scatter diagram 1617
SCATTERING 1492-1493
SCHEELE, KARL WILHELM 1493; 1152; 1205
SCHIST 1493-1494
Schistosomiasis 168
Schizophrenia 1035, 1036
SCHLEIDEN, MATTHIAS JAKOB 1494
SCHRÖDINGER, ERWIN 1494
SCHWANN, THEODOR 1494
SCIENCE 1495, *1496-1497*
SCIENCE, HISTORY OF 1498
Scientific method 1498
Sclera 591, 592
SCLERENCHYMA 1498-1499, *1499*
SCORPION 1499, *1499*
SCORPION FLY 1499-1500
SCORPIUS 1500
Screw 981, 983
Scuba diving 460
SCURVY 1500
SEA ANEMONE 1500-1501, *1500*
SEA CUCUMBER 1501
SEA HARE 1501-1502
SEA HORSE 1502, *1502*
SEA LION 1504
Sea nettle 880
Sea of Tranquillity 1355
SEA SCORPION 1504
SEA SLUG 1504
SEA SNAKE 1504

SEA SQUIRT 1505-1506, *1506*
SEA URCHIN 1506, *1506*
SEABORG, GLENN THEODORE 1501
SEAL 1502-1503, *1503*
SEALAB 1503
SEASON 1504-1505, *1505*
SEAWEED 1506-1507
Second 1055-1056
Second generation robot 1456
Second law of thermodynamics 1701-1702
Secondary circulation 1826
Secondary radar 1391
SEDATIVE 1507
SEDGE FAMILY 1507
SEDIMENTARY ROCK 1507-1508, 1457
SEED 1508-1509, *1508, 1509*
SEED FERN 1510
Segregation, law of 702-703
Seismograph 1078
SEISMOLOGY 1510, *1510*; 1246
Selection 216
Selective herbicide 781
SELENIUM 1510-1511
Self-pollination 1315
SEMICONDUCTOR 1511-1512
SENSE 1512
Sensory neuron 1143
SEPAL 1512
Series circuit 315
Serous membrane 1032
SERPENS 1512-1513
SERPENTINE 1513
SERUM 1513
SERVAL 1513-1514
Servomechanism 1453, 1455
SET THEORY 1514-1515, *1514, 1515*
SEWAGE TREATMENT 1515-1516, *1516-1517*
Sewage treatment plant 1516
SEX 1516-1517
Sex gland 800
Sextant 104
Sexual reproduction 1431-1435
SHAD 1518
Shaft mining 337
SHALE 1518
SHALLOT 1518
SHARK 1518-1519, *1518*
Shear stress 1633; 1635
SHEARWATER 1519
SHEEP 1519-1520, *1520*
Sheet lightning 944
SHELL 1520-1521, *1520, 1521*
SHELLAC 1521
SHEPARD, ALAN B., JR. 1521-1522
Shingles 300
SHIPS AND SHIPBUILDING 1522-1524, *1523*
SHOCK 1524
Shock therapy 1368
SHOCK WAVE 1524
Shockley, William 534
Short-horned grasshopper 742
SHREW 1524-1525, *1525*
SHRIKE 1525
SHRIMP 1525-1526
SHRUB 1526-1527, *1526*
Shutter 234
SICKLE CELL ANEMIA 1527
Sidereal time 1714
SIDEWINDER 1527, *1527*
SILICA 1527-1528
SILICON 1528-1529, *1528*
Silicon chip 535-536

Silicone rubber 1471
SILICONES 1529
Silk screen printing 1350
SILKWORM MOTH 1529
SILL 1529, *1529*
SILLIMAN, BENJAMIN, JR. 1530
SILT 1530
SILURIAN PERIOD 1530-1531, *1530*
SILVER 1531
Silverfish 209
Simon, Theodore 171
Simple distillation 458
SIMPLE HARMONIC MOTION 1531-1532
Simple microscope 1065
SIMULATOR 1532-1534, *1533, 1534*
Sine 1737
SINTERING 1534
SINUS 1534
SIPHON 1534-1535, *1535*
SIREN 1535
SIRIUS 1535, *1536*
SISAL 1535-1536, *1536*
SKATE 1536
SKELETON 1537-1539, *1538*
Skimmed milk 1073
SKIMMER 1539-1540
SKIN 1540-1541, *1540*
SKINK 1541, *1541*
SKINNER, BURRHUS FREDERIC 1542, *1542*
Skippers 218
SKUA 1542, *1542*
SKULL 1542, 1539
SKUNK 1542-1543, *1543*
SLAG 1543
SLATE 1543-1544, *1544*
SLEEP 1544-1546, *1545, 1546*
Slide projector 1355
SLIDE RULE 1546-1547, *1546, 1547*
SLIME MOLD 1547-1548
Slope mining 337
SLOTH 1548
SLUG 1548, *1549*
Small intestine 865
Small star 1612
SMALLPOX 1549-1550
SMELT 1550
SMELTING 1550, *1550*
Smith forging 653
SMOG 1551
Smoking 1720-1721
Smooth muscle 1122
SNAIL 1551-1552, *1552*
SNAKE 1552-1555, *1553, 1554, 1555*
SNAPDRAGON 1555
Snell's law 1427
SNOW 1555-1556
SNOW LEOPARD 1556
SNOWDROP 1556
SOAP 1556-1558, *1557*
Social bee 157-158
Social parasite 1220
Social wasp 1800
Soda-lime glass 724
SODIUM 1558-1559
SODIUM BICARBONATE 1559
Sodium borate 194-195
SODIUM CHLORIDE 1559-1560, *1559*
SODIUM HYDROXIDE 1560
Software 365
Softwood lumber 971
SOIL 1560-1561, *1561*
SOIL EROSION 1561-1563, *1562*; 371

SOIL MECHANICS 1563-1564
Soilless agriculture 826
SOLAR CELL 1564, *1564*
SOLAR ENERGY 1564-1565; 1649
Solar flare 1650-1651
Solar furnace 678; 1565
Solar heating 276
SOLAR SYSTEM 1565-1569, *1566-1567, 1568*; 1285-1286
SOLAR WIND 1569-1570
SOLDERING AND BRAZING 1570-1571, *1570*
SOLID 1571; 542; 1021
Solid fuel 669
Solid geometry 711
Solid propellant rocket 1459
SOLID-STATE PHYSICS 1571-1573, *1572*
Solitary bee 157-158
Solitary wasp 1800
SOLSTICE 1573
SOLUTION AND SOLUBILITY 1573-1574
SONAR 1574-1575, *1574*
SORGHUM 1575
SOUND 1575-1580, *1576, 1577, 1578, 1580*
Sound wave 1575-1576, 1580
Soundproofing 855
SOUTHERN CROSS 1580
Southern hemisphere 777
Sow 1274
SOYBEAN 1580-1581
SPACE 1581
Space Graph 796
Space shuttle 129
SPACE STATION 1581-1582, *1581, 1582*
Space telescope 1179
SPACE TRAVEL 1583-1586, *1583, 1584*
Spacecraft 1581-1584
SPARK PLUG 1586, *1586*
SPARROW 1586-1587, *1586*
Spastic paralysis 1218
Spathe 921
SPAWNING 1587
SPECIES 1587
SPECIFIC HEAT CAPACITY 1587-1588
SPECTACLED BEAR 1588, *1588*
Spectrograph 1590
SPECTROMETER 1588
SPECTROSCOPE 1588-1590, *1589*
SPECTRUM 1590-1591, *1590, 1589*
SPEED 1591; 7
Speed of sound 1576
SPEEDOMETER 1591-1592, *1592*
SPERM WHALE 1592
Spherical aberration 3; 928
Sphincter muscle 1123
Spicule 1650
SPIDER 1592-1595, *1593, 1594, 1595*
SPIDER MONKEY 1595, *1595*
SPINACH 1596
SPINAL CORD 1596, *1596*; 1143
Spinning 1698-1700
SPIRACLE 1596-1597
SPIRAEA 1597
Spiral galaxy 681-682
Spirillum 135
Spirit varnish 1769
SPLEEN 1597
SPONGE 1597-1598, *1597*
Spontaneous combustion 352
SPONTANEOUS GENERATION 1598
SPOONBILL 1598, *1598*
Sporangia 1547

SPORANGIUM 1598-1599, *1599*
SPORE 1599
Sporozoa 1364
SPOROZOAN 1599-1600, *1599, 1600*
SPRAIN 1600
SPRING AND GEYSER 1601-1603, *1601, 1602*
SPRING, MECHANICAL 1600-1601
SPRINGBOK 1603-1604, *1603*
SPRINGTAIL 1604
SPRUCE 1604, *1604*
Spur gear 698
SPURGE FAMILY 1604-1605, *1605*
SPUTNIK 1606, *1606*; 1486
Sputnik 1 1585
Square number 95
SQUID 1606-1607, *1607*
SQUIRREL 1607-1608, *1608*
STAINLESS STEEL 1608, *1608*; 49; 1620
STALACTITE AND STALAGMITE 1608, *1609*
STAMEN 1609, *1609*
STANDARD TEMPERATURE AND PRESSURE 1609
STANDARD TIME 1609-1610
STANDING WAVE 1610
STAR 1610-1613, *1611*
STARCH 1613-1614
STARFISH 1614, *1614*
STARLING 1614-1615, *1615*
STATES OF MATTER 1615, 1571
STATISTICS 1615-1618, *1616*
Stator 523, 524
Steady state theory 385-386, *385*
Steam condenser 366
STEAM ENGINE 1618-1619, *1618*
Steam heating 275
Steam locomotive 957, 960
Steam turbine 1746
STEEL 1619-1622, *1620, 1621*; 872
Steering 124
STELE 1622, *1623*
STEM 1623-1624, *1624*; 1294
STENTOR 1624, *1624*
Step-down transformer 1729
Step-up transformer 1729
Stereo 789; 1422
Stereo camera 237
Stereo phonograph 1422
STEREOCHEMISTRY 1624
Stereoisomer 876
STEREOPHONIC SOUND 1624-1625, *1625*; 789
STEREOSCOPE 1625-1626
Stereoscopic range finder 1414-1415
STERILIZATION 1626
STERNUM 1626
Steroid 800
STETHOSCOPE 1626
STICKLEBACK 1626-1627
STIGMA 1627
STIMULANT 1627; 478
STIMULUS 1627
Stipule 919
STOMA 1627-1628, *1628*
STOMACH 1628
STONE AGE 1628-1629, *1629*
STONE FLY 1630
STONECROP 1629, *1629*
Storage battery 153
STORK 1630
STORM 1630-1631, *1630*
STP 1609
STRATIFICATION 1631
Stratiform cloud 332
Stratigraphy 1631

Stratosphere 113
STRAWBERRY 1631-1632, *1631*
STREAMLINING 1632, *1632*
STRENGTH OF MATERIAL 1633
STRESS AND STRAIN 1633-1635, *1634*
Striated muscle 1122, 1123
String instrument 1579
Strip mining 336-337; 1079-1080
STROBOSCOPE 1635, *1635*
STRONTIUM 1635-1636, *1636*
Structural cable 221
STRUCTURAL GEOLOGY 1636
Structural isomer 876
STURGEON 1636, *1636*
Subatomic particle 1223, 1224
SUBLIMATION 1636
SUBMARINE 1637-1639, *1637, 1638*
Subtraction 94
Subtractive color mixing 349-350
SUBWAY 1639-1640, *1639*
SUCCESSION 1640
SUCKER 1640-1641, *1641*
SUCKER (fish) 1641
Sucking lice 933
SUCROSE 1641-1642, 1642
SUCTION 1642
SUCTORIAN 1642
SUGAR 1642
SUGAR BEET 1642
SUGAR CANE 1642-1643, *1643*
SULFA DRUG 1643-1644, 477
SULFATE 1644-1645, *1644*
SULFIDE 1645
SULFITE 1645
SULFUR 1645-1647, *1646, 1647*
SULFUR DIOXIDE 1647
SULFURIC ACID 1647-1648, *1647*
SULFUROUS ACID 1648
SUMAC 1648, *1648*
SUN 1648-1651, *1650, 1651*; 1565
SUN BEAR 1651, *1651*
SUNDIAL 1651-1652, *1652*; 325, 328
SUNFISH 1652
SUNFLOWER 1652, *1652*
SUNSPOT 1653, *1650, 1650*
SUPERCONDUCTIVITY 1653, *1653*; 400-401
Superconductor 399
SUPERCOOLING 1653-1654
Superfluid 776
Supergiant star 1612
SUPERNOVA 1654, *1654*; 1159
Superposition, law of 708
Superpressure balloon 141-142
SUPERSONIC FLIGHT 1654-1656, *1655*
Surface mining 1079
SURFACE TENSION 1656, *1656*
SURGERY 1656-1658, *1658*
Suspended monorail 1100
SUSPENSION 1658; 124-125
Suspension bridge 207, 209
SWALLOW 1658
SWAMP CYPRESS 1658-1659
SWAN 1659, *1659*
Swarm cell 1547-1548
SWEAT GLAND 1659
SWEET GUM 1659-1660
SWEET PEA 1660, *1660*
SWEET POTATO 1660
SWIFT 1660, *1660*
SWIM BLADDER 1661
SWITCH 1661
SWORDFISH 1661-1662, *1661*
SYCAMORE 1662, *1662*
SYMBIOSIS 1662, *1662*
Symbol (map) 1002

SYMMETRY 1663, *1663*
SYNAPSE 1663-1664
SYNCHROMESH 1664, *1664*
Synchronous satellite 1487
SYNCLINE 1664-1665
Synovial joint 883-884
SYNTHESIS 1665; 294
Synthetic dye 486-487
Synthetic fertilizer 606
Synthetic fiber 608
Synthetic resin 1437-1438
Synthetic rubber 1470-1471
Synthetic ruby 1472
Synthetic sapphire 1483
SYPHILIS 1665
Systematic poison 1308
Systolic pressure 186

T

TALC 1665-1666
Talking myna 1129
TANAGER 1666, *1666*
Tangent 1737
Tangerine 1193
Tanker 1522
TANNING 1666
TANTALUM 1667
Tap root system 1465
TAPE RECORDER 1667-1668, *1667*
Tape recording 1420
TAPEWORM 1668-1669, *1668*
TAPIR 1669, *1669*
TARANTULA 1669-1670, *1670*
TARPON 1670
TARSAL 1670
TARSIER 1670
TARTAR 1671
TARTARIC ACID 1671
TASMANIAN DEVIL 1671, *1671*
TASMANIAN WOLF 1671
TASTE AND SMELL 1672-1673, *1672*
TAURUS 1673
Tautomerism 876
TAXIDERMY 1673-1674
TAXONOMY 1674; 175
TEA 1674, *1674*
TEAK 1674
TECHNETIUM 1675
TECHNOLOGY, HISTORY OF 1675-1678, *1677*
TEETH 1678-1680, *1678*
TEFLON 1680
TELEGRAPH 1680-1681, *1681*; 355-356
TELEMETRY 1681, *1681*
Telepathy 588
TELEPHONE 1681-1684, *1683*; 164; 356
TELEPRINTER 1684
TELESCOPE 1684-1686, *1685*; 110
Telescope, radio 110
TELEVISION 1686-1690, *1687, 1689*; 1397
Television camera 237
TELLURIUM 1690
Telophase 1088
Temperate zone 323
TEMPERATURE 1690; 769; 1814
TEMPERATURE, BODY 1691-1692, *1691*
TENDON 1692
TENDRIL 1692, *1692*
Tensile stress 1633
TERBIUM 1692
Terminal ballistics 139
Terminal bud 212

TERMINAL VELOCITY 1693
TERMITE 1693-1694, *1693*
Termite colony 1694
TERN 1694-1695, *1695*
TERRAPIN 1695, *1695*
Terrestrial environment 504
Terrestrial planet 1286
TERTIARY PERIOD 1695-1696
Tesselation 1321
TESTICLE 1696
TETANUS 1696
TETRAETHYLLEAD 1696
TEXTILE 1696-1700, *1697, 1699*
THALLIUM 1700
Thallophyta 673
Thallophyte 1292
THALLUS 1700; 673
Thecodont 451
Thermal pollution 1318
Thermal reactor 1162
Thermionic emission 533
THERMISTOR 1700-1701, *1701*
THERMOCOUPLE 1701
THERMODYNAMICS 1701-1702, *1702*
THERMOMETER 1702-1704, *1703*
Thermonasty 1119
THERMONUCLEAR ENERGY 1704, *1704*
Thermonuclear power 1163
Thermonuclear reaction 1704
THERMOPILE 1705
THERMOPLASTIC 1705; 1297-1300
Thermoset 1297-1300
THERMOSETTING PLASTIC 1705
THERMOSTAT 1705, *1705*
Thigmonasty 1119
Thigmotropism 1118
Thin-layer chromatography 311
Third generation robot 1456
Third law of thermodynamics 1702
THISTLE 1706, *1706*
THIXOTROPY 1706
Thomson, Sir J.J. 518
THORAX 1706; 848
THORIUM 1706-1707
THORN, SPINE, AND PRICKLE 1707, *1707*
THRASHER 1707
THRIPS 1708, *1708*
Throttle 249
THRUSH 1708
THRUST 1708; 24
THULIUM 1708
THUNDERSTORM 1708-1710, *1709, 1710*
Thymus gland 800
Thyroid gland 799
TIBIA 1710
TICK 1710-1711, *1711*
Tidal range 1712
TIDE 1711-1712, *1711*; 1181
TIGER 1712, *1712*
TIME 1712-1715, *1713, 1714*
TIME ZONE 1715, *1715*
TIN 1715-1716, *1716*
TINPLATE 1716, *1716*
TISSUE 1716-1718, *1718*
TITANIUM 1718
TITMOUSE 1718
TITRATION 1718-1719
TNT 1719; 586
TOAD 1719-1720, *1719*
TOBACCO 1720-1721, *1720*
TOLUENE 1721
TOMATO 1721, *1721*
TOMBAUGH, CLYDE WILLIAM 1721-1722; 109; 1306
Tone arm 1422

TONSIL 1722
Tooth whale 1821
TOPAZ 1722, *1722*
TOPOLOGY 1723, *1723*
TORNADO 1724, *1724*
TORQUE 1724, *1724*
TORRICELLI, EVANGELISTA 1725
TORSION 1725, 1633
TORTOISE 1725-1726, *1726*
TOTAL INTERNAL REFLECTION
1726
TOUCAN 1726-1727, *1726*
TOUCH 1727
TOURMALINE 1727, *1727*
Tower of Babel 133
Townes, Charles H. 1014
Toxin 83
TRACE ELEMENT 1728
TRACER 1728
TRACHEA 1728, *1728*; 1443
TRADESCANTIA 1729
TRANQUILIZER 1729
TRANSDUCER 1729
TRANSFORMER 1729-1730, *1730*
TRANSISTOR 1730-1732, *1731*;
304-305; 534-535
Translocated herbicide 781-782
Transmission 124; 1426
TRANSMUTATION OF
ELEMENTS 1732
TRANSPIRATION 1732-1733, *1732*
TRANSPLANTATION 1733
TRANSURANIC ELEMENT 1733
Traumatropism 1118
TREE 1733-1736, *1734*
TREE FROG 1736, *1736*
Tree squirrel 1607
Triangle 712
Triangular number 95
TRIASSIC PERIOD 1736
TRICEPS 1736
TRICHINOSIS 1736-1737
TRIGONOMETRY 1737-1738,
1737, 1738
TRILOBITE 1738-1739, *1738*
Trinitrotoluene 1719
Triode 533; 1763
TRITIUM 1739
TROPIC 1739-1740, *1739*
TROPICAL RAIN FOREST 1740,
1740
Tropical zone 323
Tropism 1118
Troposphere 112-113
Trough 1809
TROUT 1740-1742, *1741, 1742*
Trumpeter swan 1659
TRYPANOSOME 1742
TSETSE FLY 1742
TSUNAMI 1742-1743; 496
TUBER 1743, *1743*; 1327
TUBERCULOSIS 1743-1744
TULIP 1744
TULIP TREE 1744, *1744*
Tumbler lock 955
TUNA 1744
TUNGSTEN 1745
TUNING FORK 1745
TURBINE 1745-1748, *1745, 1746,
1747*
Turbine wheel 694, 695
Turbofan engine 696
Turbo-prop engine 696
Turbotrain 957
TURBULENCE 1748
Turf grass 741
TURNIP 1748
TURNSTONE 1748
TURQUOISE 1748
TURTLE 1748-1750, *1749*

Twins 1433-1434
TYNDALL EFFECT 1750
TYPE METAL 1750
TYPHOID FEVER 1750-1751
TYPHUS 1751

U

U-235 626; 1162
U-238 1162
UFO 1754
ULNA 1751
ULTRASONIC 1751-1752, *1752*
Ultrasonic drill 474
Ultrasound 1752
Ultraviolet laser 910-911
ULTRAVIOLET LIGHT 1752
UMBILICAL CORD 1752
UNCERTAINTY PRINCIPLE
1752-1753
UNCONFORMITY 1753, *1753*
Underground mining 337; 1080
UNGULATE 1753-1754, *1753,
1754-1755*
UNIDENTIFIED FLYING OBJECT
1754
UNIT 1754, *1756*
Universal indicator 841
UNIVERSAL JOINT 1756, *1756*
UNIVERSE 1756-1758, *1757, 1758*
Unnilquadium 901
Unnilquintium 757
Upatnieks, Juris 794-795
Upset forging 653
URANINITE 1759
URANIUM 1759
URANUS 1759-1760; 109; 1288
UREA 1760; 894
URETER 1760
URETHRA 1760
UREY, HAROLD CLAYTON
1760-1761
URINE 1761; 894
Urodele 62, *61*
URSA MAJOR AND MINOR 1761
UTERUS 1761

V

V-2 rocket 204, *204*
VACCINATION 1761-1762, *1762*
Vaccine 477
VACUOLE 1762, *1762*
VACUUM 1762-1763
Vacuum pump 1376
VACUUM TUBE 1763
VALENCE 1763-1764, *1764*; 869
Valley glacier 722
VAMPIRE BAT 1764-1765, *1765*;
151
VAN ALLEN BELTS 1765-1766;
1363
VAN ALLEN, JAMES ALFRED
1765
VAN DE GRAAFF GENERATOR
1766-1767, *1766*; 8
VAN DER WAALS FORCES 1767
VAN DER WAALS, JOHANNES
1767
VANADIUM 1765
VAPOR 1767
VAPOR PRESSURE 1767-1768,
1768
VARIABLE STAR 1768, *1768*; 1612
VARNISH 1768-1769
VASCULAR PLANT 1769-1770,
1769

VECTOR QUANTITY 1770, *1770*
VEGETABLE 1770-1771
Vegetable tanning 1666
VEGETATIVE PROPAGATION
1771-1772, *1771*; 101-102
VEIN 1772-1773, *1772*
VELOCITY 1773; 7
Velocity microphone 1064
VENA CAVA 1773
Venae cavae 767
VENEREAL DISEASE 1773
Ventricle 766, 767
VENUS 1774; 109; 1288
VENUS'S-FLYTRAP 1774-1775,
1775
VERNIER SCALE 1775-1776, *1775*
VERTEBRA 1776, *1776*
VERTEBRATE 1776-1777, *1776*; 71
Vesta 103
VESTIGIAL ORGAN 1777; 580
VETCH 1777
VETERINARY MEDICINE
1777-1778, *1777*
Vibrio 135
VIBURNUM 1778
Videocassette recorder 1690
VIDEODISK 1778-1779, *1778*
Videodisk player 1690
VIDEOTAPE RECORDING
1779-1780, *1779, 1780*
View camera 237
VILLI 1780, *1780*
VINCI, LEONARDO DA
1780-1782, *1781*; 25;
125-126
VINE FAMILY 1782, *1782*
Vinegar 10
VINYL 1782
VIOLETS AND PANSIES 1782,
1783
VIPER 1783
VIREO 1783
VIRGINIA CREEPER 1783
VIRGO 1783
VIRUS 1783-1785, *1784*; 454
VISCOSITY 1785
VITAMIN 1785-1786; 444;
1172-1173
Vitamin D 1172-1173, *1173*
VOLATILE LIQUID 1786
Volcanic ash 1787
Volcanic dust 1787
Volcanic mountain 1117
VOLCANO 1786-1790, *1787, 1788,
1789, 1790*
Volcanology 1788
VOLE 1790
VOLT 1790
VOLTA, ALESSANDRO
1790-1791, *1791*; 517
VOLTAGE REGULATOR 1791
VOLTMETER 1791
VOLUME 1791
VOLVOX 1791-1792, *1791*
Vulcanization 1470
VULCANIZING 1792, *1792*
VULTURE 1792-1793, *1793*

W

WADER 1793-1794, *1794*
WAKSMAN, SELMAN ABRAHAM
1794-1795; 77
WALKINGSTICK 1795, *1795*
WALLABY 1795
WALLACE, ALFRED RUSSEL
1795-1796
Wallaroo 889

WALLEYE 1796
WALLFLOWER 1796
WALNUT 1796
WALRUS 1796-1797, *1797*
Walton, Ernest 8
Wankel engine 564
WARBLER 1797
Warm air furnace 676
Warm air heating 275
Warm front 665
WARM-BLOODED ANIMAL 1797
WARNING COLORATION 1799,
1798, 1799
WARTHOG 1799, *1799*
WASP 1799-1800, *1800*
WATER 1800-1802, *1801*; 444-446
Water bug 133
Water clock 328
Water culture 826
WATER CYCLE 1803, *1803*
Water erosion 1562-1563
WATER FLEA 1804-1805, *1805*
WATER GAS 1805
WATER GLASS 1805
WATER LILY 1805, *1805*
Water pollution 1317
WATER SOFTENING 1806, *1806*
WATER SUPPLY 1806-1808, *1807*
WATER TABLE 1808
Water treatment 1807, 1808
Water turbine 1745-1746
WATER VAPOR 1808, 1802
WATERCRESS 1803
WATERFALL AND RAPID
1803-1804, *1804*
WATSON, JAMES DEWEY 1808
Watson, John B. 1369
WATT 1808
WATT, JAMES 1808-1809; 1619
WAVE 1809-1811, *1810*
Wave motion 1811
Wavelength 1576-1577; 1809, 1810
WAX 1811
WAXWING 1811-1812, *1812*
WEASEL 1812, *1812*
WEATHER 1812-1815, *1813, 1814*;
322-323
Weather forecast 1815
Weather forecasting 1051, 1053
Weather map 33
Weather satellite 1051, 1053
WEATHERING 1815-1816, *1816*
Weaving 1700
Web-spinning spider 1595
WEBER 1816
WEBWORM 1816, *1816*
Wedge 981, 983
WEED 1816
WEEVIL 1816-1817, *1817*
WEIGHT 1817
WEIGHTLESSNESS 1818
WELDING AND CUTTING
1818-1820, *1819, 1820*
WERTHEIMER, MAX 1820; 1369
Western gray kangaroo 889
Western hemisphere 777
Western hemlock 778
Wet cell battery 153
WHALE 1820-1821
Whalebone whale 1821
WHEAT 1822-1823, *1822*
Wheatstone, Sir Charles 518
Wheel and axle 981, 983
WHIPPOORWILL 1823
WHIRLIGIG 1823-1824, *1823*
Whistling swan 1659
White dwarf star 184
White, Edward 1354
WHITEFISH 1824
WHITNEY, ELI 1824

WHITTLE, SIR FRANK 1824
WIENER, NORBERT 1824
WILLIAM, JAMES 879
WILLOW FAMILY 1825
WILTING 1825
WIND 1825-1828, *1826*, 1814-1815
Wind erosion 1563
Wind instrument 1579
WIND TUNNEL 1828, *1827*; 24
Winter bud 213
WIRE 1828, *1828*
WISTERIA 1829, *1829*
WITCH HAZEL FAMILY 1829, *1829*
Wöhler, Friedrich 54; 1198
WOLF 1829-1830
WOLFFIA 1830
WOLVERINE 1830-1831, *1830*
WOMBAT 1831, *1831*
WOOD 1831-1832, *1831*
WOOD LOUSE 1832
WOOD'S METAL 1833
WOODPECKER 1823-1833, *1832*
Woody grass 741
WOODY PLANT 1833
WOOL 1833
Work 982
Worker bee 159-160
WORM 1833-1834
WREN 1834, *1834*
WRIGHT BROTHERS 1834-1835
Wright, Orville 34; 126; 1834-1835
Wright, Wilbur 126; 1834-1835
WROUGHT IRON 1835
Wundt, Wilhelm 1369

X

XANTHOPHYLL 1835
XENON 1835; 1155
XEROGRAPHY 1835-1836, *1836*
XEROPHYTE 1836-1837
X RAYS 1837-1838, *1837*, *1838*;
1025-1026; 1401, 1402
X-RAY DIFFRACTION 1838-1839
XYLEM 1839, *1839*

Y

YAK 1839-1840
YAM 1840
YEAST 1840-1841, *1840*; 676
YELLOW FEVER 1841
Yellowstone National Park 1132
YEW 1841
Young river 1450
YTTERBIUM 1841
YTTRIUM 1841-1842
YUCCA 1842, *1842*

Z

ZEBRA 1842-1843, *1843*
ZENITH 1843
ZEOLITE 1843
Zero-pressure balloon 141, 142
ZINC 1843-1844, *1844*; 688-689
ZIRCONIUM 1844
ZODIAC 1844-1845
ZOO 1845-1846
ZOOLOGY 1846; 175
ZYGOTE 1846; 782

This work is a complete adaptation of *Encyclopedia of Nature and Science,* © 1974 Macdonald & Co. Ltd., which incorporates a completely new text and a certain number of new and additional illustrations, © 1984, 1979 Raintree Publishers Inc.

ACKNOWLEDGEMENTS

A. F. A. Colour Library; AIP Niels Bohr Library; ARDEA; (c) 1978 AURA, Inc., Cerro Tololo Inter-American Observatory; (c) 1977, 1979, 1981 AURA, Inc., Kitt Peak National Observatory; ASEA; A-Z Botanical Collection; Abbott Laboratories; Agricultural Research Council; AgriData Resources Inc.; Air Products Ltd.; Airco Welding Products; Allen Bradley Co.; Alcoa; Aldus; Allis Chalmers Corp.; American Cancer Society; Amoco; Heather Angel; ANIMALS ANIMALS/Douglas Baglin; ANIMALS ANIMALS/Mark Chappell; ANIMALS ANIMALS/ EARTH SCIENCES/E. R. Degginger; ANIMALS ANIMALS/Keith Gillett; ANIMALS ANIMALS/R. F. Head; ANIMALS ANIMALS/Robert Maier; ANIMALS ANIMALS/Patti Murray; ANIMALS ANIMALS/ John Ness; ANIMALS ANIMALS/R. Ingo Riepl; ANIMALS ANIMALS/Carl Roessler; ANIMALS ANIMALS/Leonard Lee Rue III; ANIMALS ANIMALS/J. C. Stevenson; ANIMALS ANIMALS/Jim Tuten; Ameri-Gas; Apple Computer Inc.; Aqua Magazine, Houston, Texas; Arandell-Schmidt Corporation; Asbestos Info. Committee; Associated Pres; Atkinson Morley Hospital; Atomic Energy Authority, Washington; Australia House; Australian Manne Co.; Australian News and Information Service; N. W. Ayer Incorporated; BAC; BANFF National Park; BAS; BBC Television; BEA; BICC; BOAC; Tony Bailey; Tony Baldini; Barnaby Picture Library; W. Baxter; Suzanne Beck; The Trustees of Bedford College; Belfort Instruments Co.; Carlo Belilacqua; Rudi Berkhout; Bermuda News Bureau; Bethlehem Steel Corporation; The Bettman Archive; S. C. Bisserot; Al Blankschien; Blondell-Horling Ltd.; Boeing Co.; Paul Brierley; Chris Bonnington; Bowaters Ltd.; British Airways; British Farm and Stock Breeder; British Insulated Callenders & Cables Ltd.; British Leyland; The Trustees of the British Museum; British Petroleum; The British Steel Corporation; British Tourist Authority; Maurice Broomfield; M. Bucknell; Bureau International des Poids et Mesures, France; Burlington Industries, Inc.; CERN; CEGB; CIBA; COI; CPI, St. Paul, Minnesota; The Trustees of the California Institute of Technology; Cambridge Scientific Instruments; Canada House; Canadian Government Office of Tourism; Canadian National Railways; Capital Radio; Carborundum Co.; Jack Carter; Carters Tested Seeds; Carlsbad Caverns National Park; J. Allan Cash; A. J. Castagno; Cement and Concrete Association; Charter Consolidated Services; Chevrolet Motor Division; Michael Chinery; Chubb-Brindly; Cincinnati Milacron; City of Milwaukee Health Department; Civil Aviation Authority; George Cohen; COHERENT, INC. Palo Alto, California; Bruce Coleman; John Colwell/Grant Heilman; Conservation and Development Dept., Raleigh, N. Carolina; Ken Cook Co.; C. Cooling; Copper Development Assoc.; R. J. Corbin; The Cotton Council; Courtaulds Ltd.; Conseil National de Tourisme au Libia; Gene Cox; Daily Mirror; S. Dalton; Daimler Motorkutsche; Daily Telegraph Colour Library; (c) Paul Damien; The Danish Centre; Danish Tourist Board; DECCA Records; De Beers; Degussa; David L. Denemark/Medical College of Wisconsin; Walt Disney Productions; Documentation Francaise Phototheque; Dunlop Ltd.; Ebouches S. A.; Eli Lilly Co.; English China Co.; Environment Science Service Admin.; ESSO; Robert Estall; FMC Corporation; Fairlop; Ferranti Ltd.; Fibre Glass Ltd.; Fidelity Radio Ltd.; Fisons; Florida State Tourist Board; Ford Motor Company; The Forestry Commission; Franke & Heidecke; J. R. Freeman & Co.; French National Railways; GTE—Communications Transmission Systems; John A. Garner, Mitchell Conservatory; Milwaukee; John Garner/Milwaukee County Zoo; Gates Learjet Corporation; General Electric Co.; General Motors; Geographical Magazine; German Embassy; Gilbert Photo Electrics; The Goodyear Tire & Rubber Company; The Government of W. Australia; Glasshouse Crop Research Institute; Glaxo Laboratories Ltd.; David Gow; Griffin & George Ltd.; Susan Griggs; Gronlands Geologiske Denmark; Mark Gubin; Guillemant; LuAnn Haas; Hale Observatories; Kirt Hallein/Milwaukee Publis Museum Geology Dept.; Hangurankete; Harnischfeger Corporation; Harley-Davidson Motor Co., Inc.; Roy Harris; Hawker Siddeley Photographic; Richard D. Hawthorne; Grant Heilman; Alfred Herber Ltd.; Honda Ltd.; Hoover Ltd.; Eric Hoskings; J. R. House; Sydney G. Hughes' Production; Hunting Survey and Consultant Ltd.; Hylton, Warner & Co.; IBM; ICI; IPS; IRD; Imitor Ltd.; India Tourist Office; The Institute of Geological Sciences; Institute of Ophthalmology; Instituto Nacional de Anthropologia & Historia; Mexico; Intel Corporation; International Planned Parenthood; International Wool Secretariat; Israel Government Tourist Office; Jerry D. Jacka;

Japan Information Centre; Johnson Controls, Inc.; Johnson Mathey & Co.; Morley Johnson; Kenya Tourist Board; Keystone Press Agency; Walter Kidde & Co. Inc.; Kinns Slide Centre; Kulham Electric Co.; K. P. LaGrone; Harry Lally; (c) J. Alex Langley, Jerry Frank, Ron Sefton—DPI; Frank Lane; Norman Lloyd; Lloyds Bank Ltd.; Loctite Corporation; The Trustees of the London Museum; The Library of Congress; Lockyer Collection; Lockheed Aircraft Corp.; K. Lowther; Lucasfilm Ltd.; Luray Caverns, Virginia; Macquity Collection; Malayan Rubber Fund Board; Milt and Joan Mann; Mansell Collection; Mary Evans Picture Library; Massey-Ferguson; Master Lock Company; Mike McDermot; McSpadden Photography; Medical College of Wisconsin, Department of Microbiology; Meisel Photochrome Corp.; Merchants Publishing Company; Dan Mercola; G. Metrailer Borlet; Metro Goldwyn Mayer; Milk Marketing Board; Gilbert A. Milne & Co. Ltd.; The Milwaukee Journal; Milwaukee Police Dept./Bureau of Investigation; Milwaukee Symphony Orchestra; Ministry of Defence; The MIT Museum; Yoshi Miyake; Jean Mohr; K. Moodie; Moog Music, Inc.; Pat Morris; Mount Wilson & Palomar Observatory; NASA; NHPA; NOAA/AFOS; NOAA/National Meteorological Center; National America Museum; National Bureau of Standards, United States Dept. of Commerce; National Center for Atmospheric Research; National Coal Board; National Dairy Council; National Gallery; National Oceanic and Atmospheric Administration; The National Radio Astronomy Observatory, operated by Associated Universities, Inc., under contract with the National Science Foundation; The Trustees of the National Maritime Museum; The Trustees of the National Portrait Gallery; Natural Science Photos; Hugh Newman; Novosti Press Agency; W. Neurnberg; Nitrate Corporation of Chile; Observatoire de Paris; Ohio Medical Products; Oregon State Highway Commission; Oster; Owens—Illinois; Panama Canal Co.; Paravue; Parke-Davis Co. Ltd.; Mark Paternostros; Dave Pelzer; Philback Ltd.; Philips Physical Geography; Phoebus; Photo Aquatics; Photofiles; Phototechnica; K. Pictor; Picturepoint; Pilkington Glass Manufacturers; The Pillsbury Company; Polaroid Camera Co.; Paul Popper; Port of London Authority; Port of New York Authority; Portuguese National Tourist Office; The Post Office; Press Association; Presse-und Informationsant der Bundesregiering; Brian Price; Promega Biotec; Government of Quebec; RCA; RTHPL; Raytheon Laser Center, Burlington, Massachusetts; Royal Air Force; Rickers Labs; Ricketts Encyclopaedia; Rio Tinto Zinc; Roan Selection Trust; Rockwell International; Rohm and Haas Seeds Inc.; Rolls Royce Ltd.; Ronan Picture Library; Royal Aircraft Establishment, Farnborough; Royal Botanic Gardens, Kew; Royal Astronomical Society; Royal Society of Arts; Royal Veterinary College; The Trustees of the Science Museum; Scottish Whisky Association; Seismograph Service Corps; The Shell Oil Library; J. F. Siepel, Marquette University Photographs; Sion; Dave Skoloda; Slide Centre; The Trustees of the Smithsonian Institution; Soccedada Agricolcida, Madrid; Sociedade Agricola De Portuga; Sony Corporation of America; Solarfilma; Sousse; South African Tourist Office; Stanford Linear Accelerator Center, Stanford University; Steenbeck, Inc.; Stockphotos, Inc.; Stollert & Pitt Ltd.; Janet Storms; Geri Strigenz; Juergen Strigenz; Sunkist Growers Inc.; Superior Die Set Corporation; Swiss Watch Chamber of Commerce; Swiss National Tourist Office; TBA Industrial Products Ltd.; TMS; Texas Eastman Company; Texas Instruments; Thorn Lighting; Topholm & Westerman; Transparencies Unlimited; Transworld Feature Syndication; Triumph Co.; Peter G. Tucker; Merlin Tuttle; United States Agricultural Dept.; United States Atomic Energy Authority; United States Dept. of Commerce; United States Dept. of Energy; United States Dept. of the Interior; United States Dept. of the Interior/National Park Service; United States Geological Survey; United States Information Service, Bureau of Reclamation; United States Information Agency, Washington D.C.; United States Naval Observatory; United States Naval Photographic Center; United States Travel Service; U. P. I.; T. Usbourne; Vickers Ltd.; The Trustees of the Victoria and Albert Museum; Viquier; WITI-TV; Bilhenry Walker; Michael Walker; Peter Way Ltd.; James C. Webb; Wedgewood Co. Ltd.; Werkbild Kraftwerk Union; Western Union Corporation; Wisconsin Electric; Morris Wood; Woodmansterne Ltd.; World Food, Dominica; World Health Organization; Diana Wylie; Wyoming Travel Commission; Xerox; Zenetron; Zentral Farbbild Agentur GmbH; C. Zeiss; Zoological Society, London.